READER'S DIGEST

Vegetables
for Vitality

Eat Well Live Well

READER'S DIGEST

Vegetables for Vitality

Reader's Digest

Published by The Reader's Digest Association Limited
London • New York • Sydney • Montreal

VEGETABLES FOR VITALITY is part of a series of cookery books called EAT WELL LIVE WELL and was created by Amazon Publishing Limited.

Series Editor *Norma MacMillan*
Volume Editor *Bridget Jones*
Art Director *Bobbie Colgate Stone*
Photographic Direction *Bobbie Colgate Stone, Alison Shackleton, Sheila Volpe*
Designer *Giles Powell-Smith*
Editorial Assistants *Zoe Lehmann, Anna Ward*
Nutritionists *Fiona Hunter BSc Hons (Nutri.), Dip. Dietetics, Jane Thomas BSc, M Med Sci, SRD*

CONTRIBUTORS
Writers *Sara Buenfeld, Anne Gains, Beverly LeBlanc, Sara Lewis, Sally Mansfield, Janette Marshall, Maggie Mayhew, Kate Moseley, Marlena Spieler, Susanna Tee*
Recipe Testers *Anne Gains, Clare Lewis, Heather Owen, Maggie Pannell, Susanna Tee*
Recipe Testing Co-ordinator *Anne Gains*
Photographers *Gus Filgate, William Lingwood*
Stylists *Penny Markham, Helen Trent*
Home Economists *Nicola Fowler, Louise Pickford*

FOR READER'S DIGEST
Series Editor *Christine Noble*
Editorial Assistant *Caroline Boucher*
Production Controllers *Kathy Brown, Jane Holyer*

READER'S DIGEST GENERAL BOOKS
Editorial Director *Cortina Butler*
Art Director *Nick Clark*

ISBN 0 276 42424 7

First Edition Copyright © 2000
The Reader's Digest Association Limited
11 Westferry Circus, Canary Wharf, London E14 4HE

Copyright © 2000 Reader's Digest Association Far East Limited
Philippines copyright © 2000 Reader's Digest Association Far East Limited

Notes for the reader
• Use all metric or all imperial measures when preparing a recipe, as the two sets of measurements are not exact equivalents.
• Recipes were tested using metric measures and conventional (not fan-assisted) ovens. Medium eggs were used, unless otherwise specified.
• Can sizes are approximate, as weights can vary slightly according to the manufacturer.
• Preparation and cooking times are only intended as a guide.

The nutritional information in this book is for reference only. The editors urge anyone with continuing medical problems or symptoms to consult a doctor.

Contents

Eating well to live well

Eating a healthy diet can help you look good, feel great and have lots of energy. Nutrition fads come and go, but the simple keys to eating well remain the same: enjoy a variety of food – no single food contains all the vitamins, minerals, fibre and other essential components you need for health and vitality – and get the balance right by looking at the proportions of the different foods you eat. Add some regular exercise too – at least 30 minutes a day, 3 times a week – and you'll be helping yourself to live well and make the most of your true potential.

Getting it into proportion

Current guidelines are that most people in the UK should eat more starchy foods, more fruit and vegetables, and less fat, meat products and sugary foods. It is almost impossible to give exact amounts that you should eat, as every single person's requirements vary, depending on size, age and the amount of energy expended during the day. However, nutrition experts have suggested an ideal balance of the different foods that provide us with energy (calories) and the nutrients needed for health. The number of daily portions of each of the food groups will vary from person to person – for example, an active teenager might need to eat up to 14 portions of starchy carbohydrates every day, whereas a sedentary adult would only require 6 or 7 portions – but the proportions of the food groups in relation to each other should ideally stay the same.

More detailed explanations of food groups and nutritional terms can be found on pages 156–158, together with brief guidelines on amounts which can be used in conjunction with the nutritional analyses of the recipes. A simple way to get the balance right, however, is to imagine a daily 'plate' divided into the different food groups. On the imaginary 'plate', starchy carbohydrates fill at least one-third of the space, thus constituting the main part of your meals. Fruit and vegetables fill the same amount of space. The remaining third of the 'plate' is divided mainly between protein foods and dairy foods, with just a little space allowed for foods containing fat and sugar. These are the proportions to aim for.

It isn't essential to eat the ideal proportions on the 'plate' at every meal, or even every day – balancing them over a week or two is just as good. The healthiest diet for you and your family is one that is generally balanced and sustainable in the long term.

Our daily plate

Starchy carbohydrate foods: eat 6–14 portions a day

At least 50% of the calories in a healthy diet should come from carbohydrates, and most of that from starchy foods – bread, potatoes and other starchy vegetables, pasta, rice and cereals. For most people in the UK this means doubling current intake. Starchy carbohydrates are the best foods for energy. They also provide protein and essential vitamins and minerals, particularly those from the B group. Eat a variety of starchy foods, choosing wholemeal or wholegrain types whenever possible, because the fibre they contain helps to prevent constipation, bowel disease, heart disease and other health problems.

What is a portion of starchy foods?

Some examples are: 3 tbsp breakfast cereal • 2 tbsp muesli • 1 slice of bread or toast • 1 bread roll, bap or bun • 1 small pitta bread, naan bread or chapatti • 3 crackers or crispbreads • 1 medium-sized potato • 1 medium-sized plantain or small sweet potato • 2 heaped tbsp boiled rice • 2 heaped tbsp boiled pasta.

Fruit and vegetables: eat at least 5 portions a day

Nutrition experts are unanimous that we would all benefit from eating more fruit and vegetables each day – a total of at least 400 g (14 oz) of fruit and vegetables (edible part) is the target. Fruit and vegetables provide vitamin C for immunity and healing, and other 'antioxidant' vitamins and minerals for protection against cardiovascular disease and cancer. They also offer several 'phytochemicals' that help protect against cancer, and B vitamins, especially folate, which is important for women planning a pregnancy, to prevent birth defects. All of these, plus other nutrients, work together to boost well-being.

Antioxidant nutrients (e.g. vitamins C and beta-carotene, which are mainly derived from fruit and vegetables) and vitamin E help to prevent harmful free radicals in the body initiating or accelerating cancer, heart disease, cataracts, arthritis, general ageing, sun damage to skin, and damage to sperm. Free radicals occur naturally as a by-product of normal cell function, but are also caused by pollutants such as tobacco smoke and over-exposure to sunlight.

What is a portion of fruit or vegetables?

Some examples are: 1 medium-sized portion of vegetables or salad • 1 medium-sized piece of fresh fruit • 6 tbsp (about 140 g/5 oz) stewed or canned fruit • 1 small glass (100 ml/3½ fl oz) fruit juice.

Dairy foods: eat 2–3 portions a day

Dairy foods, such as milk, cheese, yogurt and fromage frais, are the best source of calcium for strong bones and teeth, and important for the nervous system. They also provide some protein for growth and repair, vitamin B_{12}, and vitamin A for healthy eyes. They are particularly valuable foods for young children, who need full-fat versions at least up to age 2. Dairy foods are also especially important for adolescent girls to prevent the development of osteoporosis later in life, and for women throughout life generally.

To limit fat intake, wherever possible adults should choose lower-fat dairy foods, such as semi-skimmed milk and low-fat yogurt.

What is a portion of dairy foods?

Some examples are: 1 medium-sized glass (200 ml/7 fl oz) milk • 1 matchbox-sized piece (40 g/1½ oz) Cheddar cheese • 1 small pot of yogurt • 125 g (4½ oz) cottage cheese or fromage frais.

Protein foods: eat 2–4 portions a day

Lean meat, fish, eggs and vegetarian alternatives provide protein for growth and cell repair, as well as iron to prevent anaemia. Meat also provides B vitamins for healthy nerves and digestion, especially vitamin B_{12}, and zinc for growth and healthy bones and skin. Only moderate amounts of these protein-rich foods are required. An adult woman needs about 45 g of protein a day and an adult man 55 g, which constitutes about 11% of a day's calories. This is less than the current average intake. For optimum health, we need to eat some protein every day.

What is a portion of protein-rich food?

Some examples are: 3 slices (85–100 g/3–3½ oz) of roast beef, pork, ham, lamb or chicken • about 100 g (3½ oz) grilled offal • 115–140 g (4–5 oz) cooked fillet of white or oily fish (not fried in batter) • 3 fish fingers • 2 eggs (up to 7 a week) • about 140 g/5 oz baked beans • 60 g (2¼ oz) nuts, peanut butter or other nut products.

Foods containing fat: 1–5 portions a day

Unlike fruit, vegetables and starchy carbohydrates, which can be eaten in abundance, fatty foods should not exceed 33% of the day's calories in a balanced diet, and only 10% of this should be from saturated fat. This quantity of fat may seem a lot, but it isn't – fat contains more than twice as many calories per gram as either carbohydrate or protein.

Overconsumption of fat is a major cause of weight and health problems. A healthy diet must contain a certain amount of fat to provide fat-soluble vitamins and essential fatty acids, needed for the development and function of the brain, eyes and nervous system, but we only need a small amount each day – just 25 g is required, which is much less than we consume in our Western diet. The current recommendations from the Department of Health are a maximum of 71 g fat (of this, 21.5 g saturated) for women each day and 93.5 g fat (28.5 g saturated) for men. The best sources of the essential fatty acids are natural fish oils and pure vegetable oils.

What is a portion of fatty foods?

Some examples are: 1 tsp butter or margarine • 2 tsp low-fat spread • 1 tsp cooking oil • 1 tbsp mayonnaise or vinaigrette (salad dressing) • 1 tbsp cream • 1 individual packet of crisps.

Foods containing sugar: 0–2 portions a day

Although many foods naturally contain sugars (e.g. fruit contains fructose, milk lactose), health experts recommend that we limit 'added' sugars. Added sugars, such as table sugar, provide only calories – they contain no vitamins, minerals or fibre to contribute to health, and it is not necessary to eat them at all. But, as the old adage goes, 'a little of what you fancy does you good' and sugar is no exception. Denial of foods, or using them as rewards or punishment, is not a healthy attitude to eating, and can lead to cravings, binges and yo-yo dieting. Sweet foods are a pleasurable part of a well-balanced diet, but added sugars should account for no more than 11% of the total daily carbohydrate intake.

In assessing how much sugar you consume, don't forget that it is a major ingredient of many processed and ready-prepared foods.

What is a portion of sugary foods?

Some examples are: 3 tsp sugar • 1 heaped tsp jam or honey • 2 biscuits • half a slice of cake • 1 doughnut • 1 Danish pastry • 1 small bar of chocolate • 1 small tube or bag of sweets.

Too salty

Salt (sodium chloride) is essential for a variety of body functions, but we tend to eat too much through consumption of salty processed foods, 'fast' foods and ready-prepared foods, and by adding salt in cooking and at the table. The end result can be rising blood pressure as we get older, which puts us at higher risk of heart disease and stroke. Eating more vegetables and fruit increases potassium intake, which can help to counteract the damaging effects of salt.

Alcohol in a healthy diet

In recent research, moderate drinking of alcohol has been linked with a reduced risk of heart disease and stroke among men and women over 45. However, because of other risks associated with alcohol, particularly in excess quantities, no doctor would recommend taking up drinking if you are teetotal. The healthiest pattern of drinking is to enjoy small amounts of alcohol with food, to have alcohol-free days and always to avoid getting drunk. A well-balanced diet is vital because nutrients from food (vitamins and minerals) are needed to detoxify the alcohol.

Water – the best choice

Drinking plenty of non-alcoholic liquid each day is an often overlooked part of a well-balanced diet. A minimum of 8 glasses (which is about 2 litres/3½ pints) is the ideal. If possible, these should not all be tea or coffee, as these are stimulants and diuretics, which cause the body to lose liquids, taking with them water-soluble vitamins. Water is the best choice. Other good choices are fruit or herb teas or tisanes, fruit juices – diluted with water, if preferred – or semi-skimmed milk (full-fat milk for very young children). Fizzy sugary or acidic drinks such as cola are more likely to damage tooth enamel than other drinks.

As a guide to the vitamin and mineral content of foods and recipes in the book, we have used the following terms and symbols, based on the percentage of the daily RNI provided by one serving for the average adult man or woman aged 19–49 years (see also pages 156–158):

✓✓✓   or excellent   at least 50% (half)

✓✓   or good   25–50% (one-quarter to one-half)

✓   or useful   10–25% (one-tenth to one-quarter)

Note that recipes contribute other nutrients, but the analyses only include those that provide at least 10% RNI per portion. Vitamins and minerals where deficiencies are rare are not included.

Ⓥ denotes that a recipe is suitable for vegetarians.

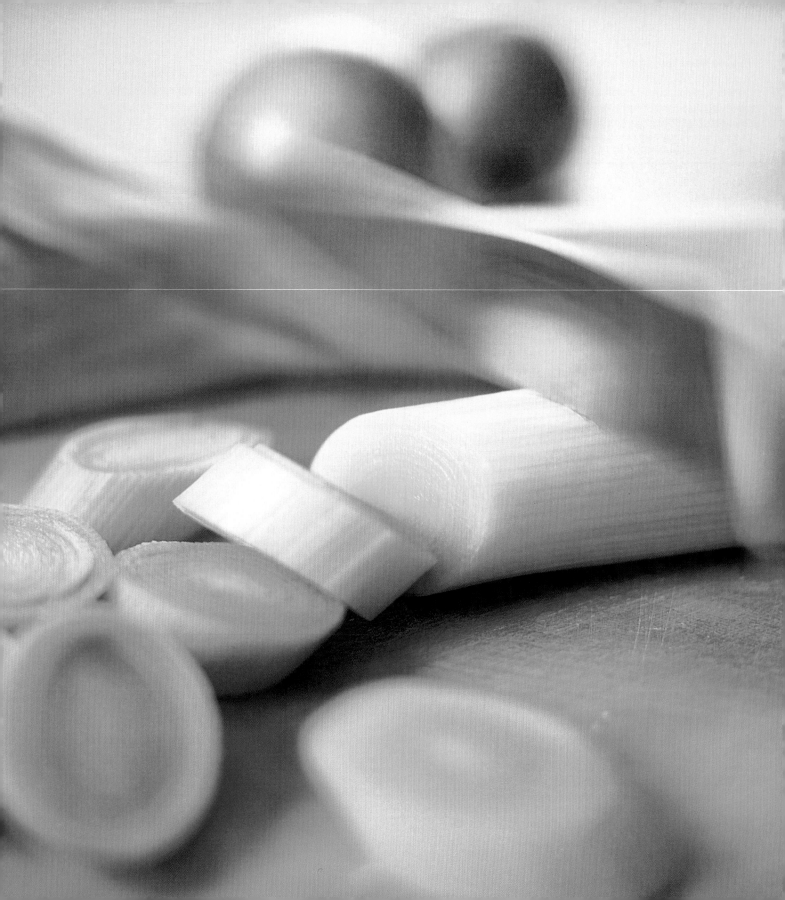

Vital Vegetables

Irresistible variety packed with goodness

VEGETABLES BRING EXCITING FLAVOURS and textures to every meal. Even better, they are packed with vitamins, minerals, protective compounds and fibre, all vital in a healthy diet. And it's not just a case of long-term benefits, because a vegetable-rich diet makes you feel great every day. Vegetables are the ultimate in versatile ingredients and essential in lots of dishes. They can be stir-fried, steamed, baked or braised as well as boiled. Most also make fabulous salads. Fresh produce requires minimum preparation – the less you do to it, the better it is for you. Frozen vegetables are good for you too. So make the most of the wonderful variety of vegetables on offer.

Vegetables in a healthy diet

Just feast your eyes on the vibrant colours and the varied shapes and textures in a vegetable display to appreciate the diversity of exciting ingredients that are available to today's cook. Making the most of vegetables in main dishes and snacks as well as accompaniments will bring health benefits along with fabulous flavour.

Why are vegetables important?

Vegetables are an essential part of a healthy, well-balanced diet. They are highly nutritious, packed with the vitamins, minerals and other compounds that protect us against illness, and they offer vital dietary fibre. All vegetables are good for us, be they fresh, frozen or canned.

In cooking, vegetables are indispensable – to create meals in their own right, as ingredients in a wealth of meat-based dishes, and as side dishes to partner fish, poultry and meat courses. They combine perfectly with nuts, grains, seeds and pulses to make delicious vegetarian meals. And adding vegetables improves the nutritional value of convenience foods – always try to serve 2 portions of vegetables with ready-prepared dishes, especially if you eat them often.

Extensive benefits

For any food to make a contribution to health, it needs to be eaten regularly and in quantity. Eating more vegetables – at least 5 portions of fruit and vegetables every day – can have a number of positive benefits.

- A vegetable-rich diet can reduce the risk of heart disease and cancer. In addition to the beneficial antioxidant vitamins and minerals present in vegetables, scientists have now discovered thousands of different plant chemicals, called phytochemicals, that are believed to have dramatic health-giving and health-protecting properties.
- Vegetables are low in sodium and many are naturally high in potassium. Most of us tend to eat too much sodium in the form of salt – much of it in processed and ready-made foods. Potassium works to balance sodium in the body, thus helping to prevent high blood pressure.
- Vegetables contain natural fibre that makes a vital contribution to good digestion and health.
- Vegetables are low in calories and fat, and ideal for making a modest quantity of protein-rich food such as meat, poultry or fish go further.

Valuable antioxidants

Vegetables and fruit are the best food sources of the antioxidants vitamin C and beta-carotene. Along with vitamin E (another antioxidant found in some vegetables), fibre and natural plant chemicals, these work to delay or even prevent oxidative damage caused by free radicals in the body.

Free radicals cause changes in blood cholesterol and damage to cells, increasing the risk of heart disease and cancer. Similar damage may also increase the risk of other problems, for example eye cataracts.

In addition to acting as an antioxidant, vitamin C is vital for a healthy immune system and healing. Beta-carotene from plant sources is converted to vitamin A (an antioxidant in its own right) in the body.

Iron-blocking brew

Drinking tea or coffee within 30 minutes of a meal reduces the absorption of iron from food, because the tannin in these drinks binds with the mineral, making it unavailable to the body. Vitamin C has the opposite effect – it enhances iron uptake – so eating or drinking foods with a good vitamin C content promotes iron absorption. Iron from vegetable sources is less easily absorbed than iron from meat, so ensuring a good supply of vitamin C is particularly important in vegetarian or other non-meat meals.

◀ The fresher the better – buy fresh vegetables in prime condition and in quantities that you will use quickly

Frozen vegetables make a valuable nutritional contribution, and they can be combined with fresh produce, for example in delicious stir-fries ▶

◀ Convenient canned vegetables bring valuable fibre to quick meals, and canned tomatoes provide lycopene, a cancer-fighting carotenoid

Vegetables for a healthy heart

Recent studies suggest that a raised level of an amino acid known as homocysteine may be closely associated with heart disease and stroke, as high levels of homocysteine can damage the cells that line the arteries. Folic acid is used in the body to convert homocysteine to another amino acid, which is used as a body-building protein, and to other substances that are essential for brain function and DNA production. When insufficient folic acid – and, less importantly, vitamins B_6 and B_{12} – is available to convert the homocysteine, the amino acid builds up in the system.

The best way to obtain the necessary folic acid is to eat foods rich in folates, which are compounds derived from folic acid. Folates are found in many vegetables, particularly dark leafy greens such as spinach and broccoli.

Green vegetables for a healthy pregnancy

Women who are trying to conceive are advised to take a folic acid supplement for 3 months before becoming pregnant and through the first 3 months of pregnancy to reduce the risk of spina bifida and related conditions in the baby. In addition to taking supplements, it is advisable to eat plenty of foods that are rich in folates such as leafy green vegetables, broccoli, Brussels sprouts and other brassicas.

Bioactive plants protecting health

Natural plant chemicals, or phytochemicals, are attracting attention for their bioactive properties, which enable them to offer protection against cancer. Much research today is focused on the glucosinolates and sulphur compounds in the brassica family – cabbage and related vegetables, such as broccoli and Brussels sprouts (see page 14). There is also great interest in the phytochemicals found in the onion family and green beans, and in bioflavonoids, the substances responsible for red and blue colours in vegetables. Some bioflavonoids act as antioxidants and also increase enzyme activity, which protects human cells against carcinogens. One of these antioxidants, called quercetin, may be more active in protecting health than vitamins C and E.

▲ Good for antioxidants – dark leafy greens such as watercress and curly kale, peas, tomatoes, peppers, pumpkin, sweet potatoes, carrots, Brussels sprouts

▼ Good for glucosinolates and sulphur compounds – cruciferous vegetables such as cauliflower, cabbage, broccoli, chard, Brussels sprouts, swede and kohlrabi

▲ Good for folates – dark leafy greens such as spring greens and watercress, cabbage, beans and spinach

▼ Good for fibre – okra, sweetcorn, fennel, peas and beans

Far more to fibre

Fresh, frozen and canned vegetables all contribute both types of essential dietary fibre. Soluble fibre can help to reduce the risk of heart disease by lowering levels of blood cholesterol. It also helps to control blood sugar levels.

Insoluble fibre softens and adds bulk to food waste passing through the gut. Helping the gut to function efficiently can prevent diverticular disease and control some types of irritable bowel syndrome. Preventing constipation also helps to avoid piles and varicose veins. A fibre-rich diet produces an environment that encourages healthy gut bacteria to grow, suppressing the growth of harmful bacteria. This process also produces a substance that suppresses cancer-cell growth.

Are convenience vegetables good for you?

While vegetables taste best and contain most nutrients when at their freshest, frozen vegetables are also excellent from a nutritional point of view. Many vegetables are frozen within hours of being picked, so they actually retain more nutrients than some 'fresh' produce that is days old before it reaches the consumer. Chilled prepared vegetables are not as rich as whole vegetables in nutrients, particularly vitamins, but they are convenient and still have some value.

Canned vegetables are processed quickly, but the high temperatures involved do reduce the vitamin content. However, they are still a useful source of dietary fibre and some phytochemicals.

Dried vegetables, which are rarely used as a main ingredient in cooking, are not an alternative to fresh produce, as they do not offer the equivalent nutritional benefits.

Vitamin pills or vegetables?

There is still a lot to be learned about exactly how fruit and vegetables actively protect our health, but we do know that the vitamins and minerals in vegetables work with the fibre and phytochemicals to boost vitality and protect against disease. Purified vitamin and mineral tablets cannot offer this advantage. And in any case, why miss out on the pleasures of eating and opt to swallow a pill instead?

Of cabbages and kings

If your usual diet includes just a few familiar green vegetables, it's time to turn over a new leaf. Discover the variety of lush leaves and succulent shoots, stalks, stems and sprouts to include in the daily 5 portions.

An ABC of shoots, stalks and leaves

Here you will find a mix of favourite vegetables with others that you may not use frequently. They are all shoots from the vegetable plant – some, like asparagus, are in the first stages of growth, while others are fully opened into leafy greens. Average portion sizes are given of the raw vegetable, although the precise quantity may vary according to the type of dish being prepared or meal being eaten.

Artichoke, globe (1 head)

In traditional herbal medicine, globe artichokes are used to aid digestion, perhaps due to their slight bitterness, which stimulates digestion. Artichokes contain some calcium.

◆ Buy heavy, plump and compact heads. They can be stored in the fridge for several days.

Asparagus (5 spears, about 125 g/4½ oz)

Asparagus is an excellent source of folate and green spears are a significant source of vitamin C. The beta-carotene content makes asparagus a useful source of vitamin A, and it offers useful vitamin E. It is known as a potent diuretic.

◆ Buy straight spears with firm tips. Store in the fridge for up to 3 days.

Eat more brassicas

The brassica group of cruciferous vegetables, which includes cabbage, cauliflower, broccoli, Brussels sprouts, kale, swede and kohlrabi, contains glucosinolates and other sulphur compounds associated with lowering the risk of cancer (see page 12). They are good sources of vitamin C and among the richest vegetable sources of folates. Eaten regularly, they also contribute appreciable amounts of minerals.

Broccoli (85 g/3 oz)

Broccoli is an excellent source of folate and vitamin C. It provides a useful amount of vitamin E, and the beta-carotene it contains also makes it a useful source of vitamin A.

◆ Buy firm, upright stalks with compact dark green heads. Store in the fridge for up to 2 days.

Brussels sprouts (85 g/3 oz)

Brussels sprouts provide beta-carotene, and they are an excellent source of folate.

◆ Buy firm, bright sprouts with tightly packed leaves. Avoid yellowing vegetables. Store in the fridge for up to 3 days.

Cabbages and greens (100 g/3½ oz)

This varied group of vegetables includes red and white cabbages, Chinese leaves, spring greens and Chinese cabbages such as pak choy. The green types are an excellent source of folate and a good source of vitamin C as well as carotenoids.

◆ Buy crisp, bright vegetables, rejecting any that are wilting, limp or yellowing. Store in the fridge for up to 2 days.

Cauliflower (85 g/3 oz)

Cauliflower contains beneficial sulphur compounds and also provides vitamin C.

◆ Buy firm heads with a few crisp leaves. Avoid discoloured or slightly soft cauliflower. Store in the fridge for up to 3 days.

Celery (½ small head, about 200 g/7 oz)

Much of celery's flavour is due to its sodium content, which is slightly higher than many vegetables; however, it also contains some potassium which balances this.

◆ Buy compact heads that are crisp. Avoid damaged or browning vegetables. Store in the fridge for up to a week.

Chicory (1 medium to large head or 2 small heads)

Bitter vegetables such as chicory have traditionally been used to stimulate digestion and aid liver and gall bladder problems.

◆ Buy firm heads with succulent-looking leaves that are not tinged brown. Store in the fridge for up to 5 days.

broccoli

asparagus

globe artichoke   Brussels sprouts

cauliflower   cabbages and greens

chicory

celery

Fennel (1 bulb, about 200 g/7 oz)

Fennel contains more phytoestrogen than most vegetables. This phytochemical is believed to help protect against breast and prostate cancers. Fennel is also a good source of potassium, and it is thought to aid digestion and relieve wind and flatulence.

◆ Buy crisp fennel, and store in the fridge for up to a week.

Kale (100 g/3½ oz)

In common with other dark green, leafy vegetables, kale is as rich in beta-carotene as orange-fleshed vegetables, but the orange colour is masked by the green pigment chlorophyll. In fact, chlorophyll may also help to protect against cancer. Kale is an excellent source of folate, and it contributes vitamin C, iron and calcium.

◆ Buy dark green leaves that look bright and fresh. Store in the fridge and use as soon as possible, within 2 days.

Kohlrabi (50 g/1¾ oz)

This purple or green-tinged vegetable looks like a root, but it is actually a swollen stem spiked with sprouting stalks and green leaves. Similar to cabbage in flavour, kohlrabi is a good source of vitamin C.

◆ Buy heavy vegetables that feel firm, and store in the fridge for up to 7 days.

Leek (75 g/2½ oz)

This most useful member of the onion family (see page 22) provides vitamin C, carotenoids and folic acid.

◆ Buy firm leeks with white bases and bright, lush green tops. Store in the fridge for up to 3 days.

Lettuces and salad leaves (about ¼ head or 1 lettuce heart)

There is a wide variety of salad leaves, including tender round lettuce, and crisp iceberg, cos, Little Gem and romaine. There are frilly varieties, such as Lollo Biondo, and red-tinged leaves, for example Lollo Rosso and Oak Leaf. Lamb's lettuce and frisée (the popular name used for curly endive) are also readily available. Rocket and other strongly flavoured leaves can be mixed in small quantities with more delicate salad leaves. The darker outer leaves contain more vitamins and antioxidants than paler inner leaves.

◆ Buy whole rather than prepared, torn heads, which will have lost a lot of their vitamin C and folate content. Avoid wilting or brown leaves. Store in the fridge for up to 4 days.

vital vegetables

fennel

kale

lettuces and salad leaves

kohlrabi

leeks

chard

spinach

sprouted seeds

watercress

Spinach and chard (200 g/7 oz)

Both of these leafy greens provide vitamin C and folate, and they are the richest sources of a particular type of carotenoid called lutein. Evidence suggests that lutein offers protection against a common cause of blindness in older people. Spinach also makes a useful contribution of iron, and it provides vitamin E. Remember that the chard stalks should be eaten too. Although not offering all the same nutrients as the green leaves, they are a good source of fibre.

◆ Buy fresh bright leaves. Avoid wilting, yellowing or crushed leaves. Store in the fridge and use within 2 days.

Sprouted seeds (45 g/1½ oz)

The nutritional content varies according to the type of seeds or beans used. Bean sprouts grown from mung beans provide some vitamin C and B vitamins.

◆ Buy fresh-looking sprouts, avoiding any that are limp and brown or stained. The sprouts should smell pleasantly fresh. Store in the fridge for up to 3 days.

Watercress (1 bunch, about 80 g/scant 3 oz)

Watercress has high levels of carotenoids and offers vitamins C and B_6 It also makes a contribution to mineral intake, providing iron and some zinc, potassium and calcium. Serve watercress raw and in generous portions – for example, as a main ingredient in a salad – to make the most of its nutritional benefits. Use the tender stalks as well as the leaves, as they are tasty and nutritious too.

◆ Buy glossy, dark green watercress in bunches, if available, rather than ready-trimmed and washed. Avoid yellowed leaves. Store in the fridge and use within 2 days.

Sea vegetables

Seaweed is best known as a popular vegetable in Japanese cooking, but it also features in Western cuisines. British seaweeds include Welsh laverbread and Irish carragheen. Samphire, or glasswort, a salty green vegetable that resembles long, thin, 'jointed' beans, is a shore plant rather than a seaweed. Most types of seaweed are rich in iodine, and they contain other minerals, including calcium, iron, potassium and zinc. Some also have a high sodium content.

vital vegetables

Picked from the plant

Full of food value and flavour, and with a diversity of exciting textures, these are the ingredients that bring vegetable cuisine to life. They are ideal for all sorts of different cooking methods: you can stir-fry or steam them, stuff or stew them, braise or barbecue them, and their characteristics always shine through.

An ABC of vegetable fruits

These bright and varied vegetable fruits are so called because they carry the seeds of the plant on which they grow. In some cases they actually are the seeds – as in peas, for example. Average portion sizes of the raw vegetable are given as a guide.

Aubergine (1 small or ½ large)

Aubergines may be the familiar rich purple or have white, green or striped violet skin, and in shape they may be long and slim, plump ovals or little balls. Aubergines add satisfying bulk to dishes, yet are very low in calories.

◆ Buy plump, firm vegetables with a smooth, glossy skin. Store in the fridge for up to a week.

Avocado (½ medium)

These are unusual among vegetables in that they have a high fat content, but most of the fat is monounsaturated, so they share the 'good' fat profile of nuts. Avocados also contain vitamin E and the B-group vitamins B_1, B_2 and B_6. They provide a useful source of vitamin C and some folate and potassium, and are extremely low in sodium.

◆ If bought hard, place in a paper bag and ripen at room temperature. Store ripe avocados in the fridge for up to 2 days.

Broad beans (85 g/3 oz)

Broad beans contain twice as much fibre as green beans and are a good source of quercetin, the phytochemical linked with lowering the risk of heart disease. They also provide beta-carotene, vitamin C and many of the B vitamins.

◆ Buy plump, fresh-looking pods that feel firm (so you know they will contain good beans). Very large, pale-coloured pods will contain large beans that may be tough, and these will probably need to be skinned after cooking. Store broad beans in the fridge and use within 2 days.

Chillies

Although the many types of hot chillies are used mainly as a spice or flavouring ingredient, there are also milder varieties that are cooked as the main vegetables in a variety of dishes.

◆ Buy and store as peppers.

Courgette and vegetable marrow (100 g/3½ oz)

Courgettes provide vitamins C and B_6, folate and beta-carotene. It is important to eat the skins as they are the main source of these nutrients. Marrow has a high water content, which means that it provides satisfying bulk with few calories.

◆ Buy firm vegetables that feel heavy for their size. Store in the fridge for up to 5 days.

Cucumber (¼ medium)

Cucumber is refreshing and distinctive in flavour. It has a high water content and is a mild diuretic.

◆ Buy green glossy cucumbers that are rigid, and store in the fridge for up to 5 days.

Green beans (85 g/3 oz)

There are many varieties including runner, French and bobby beans. Green beans are a significant source of folate. Runner beans contain the most vitamin C, providing a useful source.

◆ Buy firm, crisp beans that snap rather than bend – they should be young, tender and a good fresh green colour. Avoid very large, blemished or tired-looking beans. Store in the fridge for up to 5 days.

Mushrooms (50 g/1¾ oz)

Mushrooms contain a good combination of the B vitamins B_2, niacin and pantothenic acid, and they provide copper and potassium. Mushrooms are unlike other vegetables, as they are part of the vast family of fungi. Although they are not usually grouped with vegetable fruits of plants, they are the spore-bearing part of the mushroom organism and responsible for dispensing the fungi equivalent of seeds.

avocado

broad beans

chillies

aubergines

marrow, courgettes and courgette flowers, patty pan squashes

cucumber

mange-tout, peas and sugarsnaps

okra

green beans

mushrooms

Peas, petit pois, mange-tout and sugarsnap peas (75 g/2½ oz)

Peas are a useful source of vitamin C and fibre, particularly soluble fibre. Mange-tout and sugarsnap peas are richer sources of both vitamin C and fibre because the pods are eaten too. Unusually, peas also contribute B vitamins, in particular B_1, and their protein content is high for a vegetable that also provides a useful amount of folate. Mange-tout are not as good a source of protein as the peas are not developed. In addition, peas are a useful source of iron and zinc. Frozen peas can contain as much vitamin C as fresh peas, and are one of the most nutritious processed foods.

◆ Fresh pea pods should be bright green and firm. Store in the fridge for up to 5 days. Shell peas just before use.

Pepper (½–1 pepper or 75 g/2½ oz)

These are an excellent source of vitamin C – half a raw pepper provides over twice the RNI of this vitamin. Red peppers are an excellent source of beta-carotene, and all peppers also contain a small amount of vitamin E.

◆ Buy glossy, crisp and unwrinkled peppers. Store in the fridge for up to 10 days.

◆ Buy firm, dry mushrooms. Store unwashed in a paper bag in the fridge for up to 5 days.

Okra (85 g/3 oz)

Also known as ladies' fingers, these multi-sided pods provide vitamin C, some carotenoids and folate. They are also a source of calcium and potassium.

◆ Buy pods that look fresh and feel firm. Avoid limp, wrinkled or blemished pods, and those that look very large and tough. Store in the fridge for up to 3 days.

peppers

Cultivated mushrooms

Mushrooms grow rapidly, developing from small buttons, to closed cap, to open and large open mushrooms. As they grow, they darken and become stronger in flavour. Brown cap mushrooms are a different variety, darker and with a slightly stronger flavour. Other common types include delicate oyster and distinctively flavoured shiitake mushrooms.

Pumpkin and other squashes (75 g/2½ oz)

Related to marrows and courgettes, there are many types of squash, from the homely pumpkin to attractively shaped patty pan and spaghetti squash with its pale golden strands of flesh. The nutritional value varies according to type. For example, acorn squash provides some vitamin A, pumpkin supplies a useful amount and butternut squash is an excellent source. Squashes can also be a useful source of vitamin C.

◆ Buy firm vegetables that are heavy for their size, with hard skins according to variety, preferably whole rather than in cut portions. Store whole hard-skinned squash in a cool, dry, airy place, ideally hanging in a net bag. In the right conditions it will keep for several months. Store cut pieces and squashes with edible skin in the fridge for up to 5 days.

Sweetcorn (1 cob or 85 g/3 oz kernels)

Popular fresh as corn-on-the-cob and frozen or canned as kernels, sweetcorn, a variety of maize, makes a valuable contribution to fibre and folate intake, and also contains vitamins B_1, B_6 and C.

◆ Buy cobs with firm, plump kernels. Avoid any that look dried and withered. Store in the fridge for up to 5 days.

Tomato (2 medium)

Tomatoes are an excellent source of vitamin C and a significant source of vitamin A from beta-carotene. The colour in the skin is mainly from another carotenoid called lycopene, a powerful antioxidant. Cooking and processing release lycopene from the skin, so there is more in tomato products such as purée, ketchup, passata and canned tomatoes than in raw tomatoes.

◆ Buy firm, ripe fruit in small quantities and store at room temperature. If tomatoes are refrigerated, let them come to room temperature before eating.

Nuts

Nuts are the fruit seeds of plants contained in hard protective shells. They are high in unsaturated fat, with very small amounts of saturated fat. Coconut is the exception, with a high saturated fat content. Nuts provide vitamin E, folate, phytochemicals, protein and useful amounts of the minerals iron, selenium and zinc (amounts differ according to the type of nut). Nuts are also high in fibre. Eating as little as 30 g (1 oz) of walnuts per day has been shown to reduce harmful levels of blood cholesterol and also to influence the type of cholesterol present, increasing beneficial cholesterol while reducing the harmful type.

pumpkin and squashes

sweetcorn

tomatoes

Back to your roots

We take many roots, tubers and bulbs for granted as they make their valiant contribution to balanced eating.

Remember that there are many vegetables of this type to bring satisfying goodness throughout the year.

An ABC of roots, bulbs and tubers

The main role of starchy roots and tubers is to provide plenty of good-to-eat complex carbohydrate. Other roots offer complementary nutrients. When eaten regularly and in quantity, these vegetables are beneficial in many ways. Average portion sizes of the raw vegetable are given as a guide.

Beetroot (2 small or 1 large)

Richly coloured beetroot contains potassium and folate as well as iron. It is low in calories and, like other vegetables, provides useful fibre.

◆ Buy firm, dry beetroot that look plump, but not too big, and feel hard. Remove the leaves, then store in the fridge for up to 5 days. Vacuum-packed cooked beetroot (without vinegar or other acid added) is true to the flavour of freshly boiled, and it has a long shelf life in the sealed pack. Traditionally, freshly harvested beetroot leaves were cooked in the same way as spinach, but it is mainly the root that is used today.

Carrot (55 g/2 oz)

The large amount of beta-carotene and other carotenoids in carrots, particularly in old or main-crop vegetables, make this vegetable an excellent source of vitamin A. The beta-carotene is much better absorbed by the body (and converted into vitamin A) if the carrots are cooked.

◆ Buy crisp, firm carrots with a good orange colour. If the carrots have tops, these should be bright green and fresh. Store in the fridge for up to a week.

Celeriac (75 g/2½ oz)

With a flavour similar to celery, but lighter, this root is low in sodium and a reasonable source of fibre. It also contains some vitamin C, B_1, folate and potassium.

◆ Buy firm, heavy celeriac, and store in the fridge or a cool, dark place for up to a week.

Jerusalem artichoke (100 g/3½ oz)

Similar in size and colour to new potatoes, Jerusalem artichokes are high in fibre and contain copper and potassium.

◆ Buy firm roots and store unwashed as for potatoes.

Onions and their family

Onions, shallots, leeks (see page 16), spring onions, garlic and chives all contain several beneficial phytochemicals. One of these, quercetin, is associated with lower rates of heart disease and stroke. Another, allicin, is believed to assist in lowering blood cholesterol levels, thus preventing blood clots from forming and lowering blood pressure.

◆ Buy hard, well-shaped onions with dry, papery skins. Avoid any that are soft, discoloured or sprouting. Store in a cool, dark place that is dry and airy. In the right conditions onions will keep for several weeks. Spring onions should be bright and firm – avoid any that look wilted or slightly slimy. Store spring onions in the fridge for up to 5 days.

Parsnip (75 g/2½ oz)

Slightly sweet, full-flavoured parsnips contain some vitamin C. They also provide folate.

◆ Buy small to medium parsnips. Avoid any that are soft, with wrinkled skin or brown patches. Store in a cool, dark, dry and airy place for up to 10 days.

Potato (1 medium)

There is a wide variety of new, salad and main crop potatoes, and the choice depends on the cooking method. Potatoes are an excellent starchy carbohydrate food. Eaten daily in good quantity, they are a useful source of vitamin C and they also contribute iron and B vitamins. The skin and the area immediately below it contain the most nutrients. New potatoes contain more nutrients than old crop vegetables.

◆ Buy potatoes loose or in paper bags, if possible. If in polythene bags, avoid any that have been 'sweating' and look moist, and potatoes that are sprouting or green. Remove from polythene bags to a paper bag for storage. Keep potatoes in a cool, dark, dry place for up to 2 weeks. There is no need to wash them before storage.

Radish (50 g/1¾ oz)

Large white radish (mooli or daikon) is now as widely available as the small red radishes familiar in salads. The latter are a useful source of vitamin C.

◆ Buy firm, bright-skinned radishes; white radish should look moist and fresh. Store in the fridge for up to 5 days.

Swede (75 g/2½ oz)

One of the brassica family, swede offers the same benefits (see page 14) and in addition is a useful source of vitamin C.

◆ Buy firm swede that looks fresh and feels heavy. Store in the fridge for up to a week or as for potatoes.

Jerusalem artichokes

beetroot

carrots

celeriac

parsnips

potatoes

the onion family

radishes

swedes

sweet potatoes

turnips

Sweet potato (100 g/3½ oz)

Sweet potatoes are a delicious starchy carbohydrate. Orange-fleshed varieties are a good source of beta-carotene, which the body can convert into vitamin A. All sweet potatoes provide vitamins C and E, potassium and fibre.

◆ Buy firm sweet potatoes with no soft patches. Store in the fridge for up to a week or as for potatoes.

Turnip (75 g/2½ oz)

This slightly peppery root vegetable is similar to swede in vitamin C content.

◆ Buy hard, crisp turnips that are heavy for their size. If they have green tops, these should be bright and crisp. Store in a cool, dark, airy place, or in the fridge, for up to a week.

Vegetable basics

Treat your vegetables well and they will reward you in taste, texture and nutritional benefits. Use them at their peak of freshness, enjoying them raw or cooking them by a method that preserves maximum vitamins.

Speedy turnover – fresh and fast

The vitamins and minerals in vegetables are at peak levels when the produce is first harvested, so buy the freshest possible vegetables, in quantities you will consume quickly. Keep frozen vegetables as back-up for times when you run out of fresh, rather than storing fresh produce for too long.

The fridge is the best storage place for most vegetables. The exceptions are root vegetables, such as potatoes, parsnips and onions, and hard-skinned squashes, which keep best in a cool, dark and dry place.

Golden rules for preparing vegetables

- Prepare as close to cooking or eating as possible. Once cut, oxidation causes loss of vitamin C from vegetables exposed to air – sprinkling with lemon juice helps to reduce this.
- Wash vegetables thoroughly but quickly. Never soak them, because water-soluble vitamins will seep out and then be drained away.
- When possible, eat the peel or skin, as nutrients are often concentrated just under it. The skin also provides fibre.
- Prepare vegetables for boiling or steaming in large pieces rather than cutting them into small cubes or slices. There is then less surface area from which nutrients can be lost.
- When cooking vegetables in water, save the cooking liquid and use it, within a day or two, in soups or sauces.
- Whether boiling, steaming, frying or grilling, be sure not to overcook crisp green and yellow vegetables. Not only does it destroy even more of the vital vitamin content, but it leaves the vegetables limp and flavourless.

Cooking know-how
Boiling

Use the minimum of water and add vegetables to boiling water (rather than covering them with cold water and bringing to the boil), to shorten the time for nutrients to seep out. Pour just enough boiling water over root vegetables to cover them. Never add bicarbonate of soda to the cooking water – it is an old-fashioned method of preserving the vegetable's colour, but it destroys vitamin C. Simmer or boil for the shortest possible time. Drain and serve immediately.

▼ Wash vegetables quickly in a colander under cold running water

How does cooking affect vitamins and minerals?

Beta-carotene (which is converted into vitamin A by the body) is stable during mild heating, but losses occur at high temperatures.

Vitamin C leaches out during cooking because it is water soluble and it is also heat sensitive, so some is destroyed.

Water-soluble B vitamins are lost if the cooking water is discarded.

Vitamin E is destroyed at high temperature.

Minerals are not destroyed by heating, but they dissolve in water and seep out into the cooking liquid.

Nutrients are lost when food is left standing, kept warm or reheated.

Baked potato wedges

These super-chunky oven chips are a great alternative to deep-fried chips. Preheat the oven to 240°C (475°F, gas mark 9) and heat a roasting tin in the oven. Cut scrubbed potatoes (with the skin) into big wedges and place them in a polythene bag. Add 1–2 tbsp sunflower or extra virgin olive oil (or just enough to coat the potatoes lightly) and seasoning to taste (dried herbs and fennel seeds are good too), then shake the bag to coat the potatoes. Tip them into the hot roasting tin and bake for 45–50 minutes, turning once or twice, until the potato wedges are crisp and well browned. Serve hot.

▲ Steam vegetables until they are just tender but still firm

Steaming

This moist method takes slightly longer than boiling, but because the vegetables are not immersed in water there is less loss of water-soluble vitamins and minerals. The maximum vitamins and minerals are retained if the vegetables are sealed in a foil parcel, otherwise some nutrients will be lost by seepage into moisture as the steam condenses and drips back into the pan.

Braising and stewing

Most types of vegetables can be cooked this way, either singly or mixed. Start by cooking those that take longest, and add vegetables that cook quickly towards the end. Use a small amount of liquid and serve it with the vegetables.

Stir-frying

Being quick and using the minimum of liquid and fat, this is a very good method for preserving maximum nutrients. Cut up the vegetables just before cooking. Stir-fry frozen vegetables from frozen. Serve any cooking juices with the vegetables.

Frying

With a non-stick pan and just enough of a monounsaturated or polyunsaturated vegetable oil to prevent the vegetables from sticking to the pan, frying can be a good cooking method for vegetables.

Steaming in foil packets
retains vital nutrients

Grilling

This is good for all sorts of vegetables, particularly peppers, aubergines, mushrooms and courgettes. Brush them with the minimum of oil and cook under a preheated grill. Grilling on a flameproof dish is a useful way of preserving juices.

Baking and roasting

These are perfect methods for preserving water-soluble nutrients and are ideal for a wide variety of vegetables. Roots, vegetable fruits, stalks and shoots all cook well this way. Leafy vegetables can be baked when rolled around a stuffing.

Making the most of vegetables

Bring cooking methods and seasonings for vegetables right up to date, then serve in generous portions. For example, enjoy traditional-style meals by updating 'meat and 2 veg' to '3 veg and meat'. Serve smaller portions of meat with plenty of starchy carbohydrate, such as pasta, rice or potatoes, and add a selection of lightly cooked vegetables or extra-large portions of a single favourite. Try making vegetable-based, non-meat meals part of your regular diet – a simple baked potato piled with stir-fried vegetables, or a risotto or pasta with succulent roast vegetables will tempt all the family. Try the ideas below for boosting the vegetable content of everyday meals.

- Enliven traditional meat or poultry casseroles with peppers, carrots, courgettes, aubergine, celery, celeriac, mushrooms, green beans and peas.
- Pack sandwiches with crunchy vegetable mixtures. The classic mixture of tomato, cucumber, lettuce and watercress can be enhanced with grated carrot, radishes, strips of pepper or coarsely shredded red or white cabbage.
- Frozen vegetables are a real asset in salads: peas, green beans, broad beans and sweetcorn (individually or mixed) are perfect with diced cucumber, chopped spring onion, tomato, watercress or rocket piled on a base of green leaves. Cook the frozen vegetables in boiling water for 2–3 minutes, then drain well and toss with a little dressing. You do not even have to wait for them to cool – just mix with the raw salad vegetables and serve.

Child-friendly vegetable ideas

Set children off to a good start by making appealing vegetable-packed meals a way of life. Canned baked beans are always popular, and a good partner for vegetables: serve them in baked potatoes or use them as a base for frozen mixed vegetables. Here are some more ideas.

- Extend the meat mixture for burgers by adding lots of grated carrot and chopped celery.
- Add brightly coloured vegetables, such as peppers, tomato, peas and sweetcorn, to frozen pizza.
- Add extra diced carrot, peppers and chopped tomatoes to spaghetti bolognese.
- Include sliced or grated vegetables in all sandwiches.
- Cut up sausages or beefburgers into bite-sized pieces and thread onto skewers with chunks of red pepper, mushrooms, baby sweetcorn, courgette and other vegetables. Grill or cook on the barbecue.
- Add peas, diced carrot, shredded cabbage, broccoli florets and other vegetables to the minced meat mixture for a cottage or shepherd's pie.
- Cook swede, carrots and parsnips with potatoes for mashing.

Children's favourites: burgers or sausages on vegetable kebabs, and sandwiches packed with crunchy vegetables

speedy pizza with added canned and frozen vegetables

quick raita for Indian meals

fresh salsa for Mexican meals

Oriental-style salad for Chinese meals

Easy and convenient

When using convenience foods and ready-made or take-away meals, you can enhance their flavour and nutritional value very simply by adding vegetables. For example, serve frozen peas or sliced tomatoes with fish and chips, or frozen peas and sweetcorn or frozen mixed vegetables with fish fingers. Here are some more quick and easy ideas.

• Top pizza bases with well-drained canned chopped tomatoes (look for the varieties with herbs, spices and garlic added) and add frozen vegetables – chopped spinach, broccoli, peas and sweetcorn are all good. Add a little grated cheese or a light sprinkling of breadcrumbs for a crispy top.

• Add a thick layer of sliced courgette and tomato to bought lasagne, then sprinkle with a little grated Parmesan cheese before putting in the oven. A fresh, crisp salad is a must with lasagne as the two are superb partners.

• Top bought quiche with a layer of vegetables and bake until the quiche is hot and the vegetables are cooked. Try sliced mushrooms and tomatoes with strips of colourful peppers or sliced courgettes.

• Fill bought pancakes or flour tortillas with chopped frozen spinach (no need to thaw first, just leave the frozen 'nuggets' whole) mixed with low-fat soft cheese and chopped spring onions. Roll up around the filling, place in a dish and pour over 1–2 cans chopped tomatoes with herbs. Sprinkle with a little grated cheese and bake.

• Always serve a big fresh salad with burgers or pizza.

• Make a delicious raita-style salad to go with take-away or ready-prepared Indian dishes. Combine plenty of diced cucumber, chopped spring onion, grated carrot and chopped watercress or fresh coriander with plain low-fat yogurt. Sprinkle with chopped fresh mint and a little chilli powder.

• Mix up a quick salsa to go with Mexican meals. Dice lots of tomato, cucumber, onion and celery, then mix and season. Add diced fresh chilli and chopped fresh coriander.

• Serve a simple Oriental-style salad with Chinese meals. Mix fresh bean sprouts and chopped spring onions with canned bamboo shoots and sliced water chestnuts. Serve on Chinese leaves or shredded pak choy and dress with a few drops of toasted sesame oil and soy sauce.

vital vegetables

Vegetable stock

Use this light stock as a base for delicate soups and sauces, and in risottos and similar dishes. It will keep in the fridge for up to 5 days or in the freezer for up to 1 month.

Makes about 1.7 litres (3 pints)

15 g (½ oz) butter
225 g (8 oz) leeks, chopped
225 g (8 oz) onions, chopped
1 large bay leaf
several sprigs of fresh thyme
several sprigs of fresh parsley, stalks bruised
225 g (8 oz) carrots, diced
150 g (5½ oz) celery, diced
1 tsp salt
5 black peppercorns

Preparation time: 15 minutes
Cooking time: 1 hour

1 Melt the butter in a large saucepan or stockpot over a moderate heat. Stir in the leeks and onions, then reduce the heat to low. Cover with a tight-fitting lid and leave the vegetables to 'sweat' for 20 minutes without lifting the lid.
2 Tie the herbs together into a bouquet garni. Add it to the pan with the carrots, celery, salt, peppercorns and 2 litres (3½ pints) of cold water. Increase the heat and bring slowly to the boil, skimming the surface if necessary to remove any scum. As soon as the water boils, reduce the heat to low and simmer for 35 minutes.
3 Strain the stock into a large heatproof bowl and set aside to cool. Use immediately, or transfer to tightly sealed jars or freezer containers for storage.

Another idea

• To make a rich roasted vegetable stock, omit the butter and leeks. Increase the quantity of onions to 900 g (2 lb) and carrots to 450 g (1 lb). Instead of sweating the onions as in step 1, roast them with the carrots. Preheat the oven to 220°C (425°F, gas mark 7) and toss the onions and carrots with 1 tbsp extra virgin olive oil in a flameproof casserole. Roast the vegetables for 40 minutes, stirring twice. Add the remaining ingredients and follow steps 2 and 3 to finish the stock. To further enrich the stock, add 10 g (¼ oz) dried porcini mushrooms and 1 tbsp dry sherry with the water.

Light mashed potatoes

This plain mash is flavoured with a hint of bay and enriched with a little olive oil instead of butter.

Serves 4
125 ml (4½ fl oz) milk
1 bay leaf
900 g (2 lb) floury potatoes, such as King Edward or Maris Piper, peeled and cut into chunks
2 tbsp extra virgin olive oil
salt and pepper

Preparation time: 15 minutes
Cooking time: 15–20 minutes

1 Place the milk, bay leaf and a pinch of salt in a small saucepan. Heat gently until just boiling, then remove from the heat and set aside to infuse while you cook the potatoes.
2 Place the potatoes in a saucepan and pour over boiling water to cover by 5 cm (2 in). Bring back to the boil, then reduce the heat and cook for 15–20 minutes or until the potatoes are very tender.
3 Drain the potatoes, shaking the colander or sieve to remove any excess water, and return them to the pan. Discard the bay leaf and pour the milk over the potatoes.
4 Mash the potatoes until they are completely smooth. Add the olive oil, then beat in seasoning to taste. Serve immediately.

Some more ideas
• To make a parsley mash, omit the bay leaf used to flavour the milk. Finely chop 55 g (2 oz) parsley – or less if you prefer – and add to the potatoes with the olive oil.
• Dill and lemon mash is excellent with fish or poultry dishes. Replace the bay leaf with the finely grated zest of ½ lemon. Do not strain the zest out of the milk. Beat 4 tbsp finely chopped fresh dill into the mash with the seasoning.
• For a garlic mash, infuse 1 garlic clove, crushed, in the milk instead of the bay leaf. Strain the milk into the potatoes.
• Cardamom sweet potatoes are delicious with grilled or roast poultry or meat, especially pork. Cover 450 g (1 lb) sweet potatoes, cut into 2.5 cm (1 in) dice, with boiling water and add 1 bay leaf and 2 green cardamom pods, crushed. Cook for 10 minutes or until very tender. Drain, reserving 3 tbsp of the cooking liquid; discard the flavourings. Mash until smooth with the reserved liquid, then add a little freshly grated nutmeg and seasoning to taste.

Making More of Vegetables

Vitamin-rich snacks, starters and drinks

VEGETABLES MAKE WONDERFUL SOUPS. Try a chunky soup full of root vegetables and leeks, or for hot days, ring the changes by adding asparagus and peas to a classic iced vichyssoise. Vegetables also make refreshingly different drinks. For breakfast, whiz up a yogurt smoothie with beetroot, raspberries and cranberry, or enjoy a zesty red pepper pick-me-up at any time of day. Pack sandwiches with grilled or roasted vegetables. For superb snacks, make irresistible carrot bread – ideal with savoury fillings – or sweet American-style muffins with grated courgettes.

Tomato and citrus blush

This wonderfully tangy drink is refreshing for breakfast or brunch or as a pick-me-up at any time of day. It also makes an excellent alcohol-free alternative to a cocktail before lunch or dinner. It is best made with sweet, full-flavoured tomatoes, preferably vine-ripened, and perfectly ripe mango.

Serves 4

1 ripe mango

500 g (1 lb 2 oz) tomatoes, skinned, halved and seeded

600 g (1 lb 5 oz) watermelon, peeled, seeded and cut into chunks

grated zest and juice of 1 orange

grated zest and juice of 1 lime

To serve

ice

orange and lime slices

borage or sage flowers (optional)

Preparation time: 25 minutes

1 Peel the skin off the mango, then cut the flesh away from the flat central stone. Coarsely chop the flesh.

2 Put the chopped mango, tomatoes, watermelon, and orange and lime zest and juice in a food processor or blender and purée until smooth. Depending on the capacity of your blender, you may have to do this in 2 batches.

3 Half fill 4 large tumblers with ice and pour over the tomato and citrus blush. Garnish with orange and lime slices and borage or sage flowers, if available. Serve immediately.

Some more ideas

• For a summer starter, serve the drink in bowls as a cold soup. Omit the ice cubes and orange and lemon slices, and swirl in a little plain low-fat yogurt.

• To make a gazpacho quencher, skin, seed and roughly chop 250 g (9 oz) tomatoes. Roughly chop a 5 cm (2 in) piece of cucumber, 1 celery stick, 2 spring onions and 1 garlic clove. Purée the chopped ingredients with 200 g (7 oz) passata. Stir in 2 tsp balsamic vinegar and 250 ml (8½ fl oz) still mineral water. Half fill 4 tall tumblers with ice and pour in the drink. Serve with long thin celery sticks, for stirring, and top with a sprinkling of chopped spring onions and diced tomato.

Plus points

• Tomatoes, ripe mangoes and watermelon all provide vitamin C, an important nutrient for maintaining immunity and promoting healthy skin.

• Mango also provides beta-carotene, which the body converts to vitamin A. The beta-carotene content increases as the fruit ripens and its colour darkens. Vitamin A is essential for healthy skin and good vision, especially in dim light.

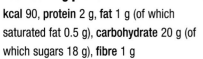

Each serving provides

kcal 90, **protein** 2 g, **fat** 1 g (of which saturated fat 0.5 g), **carbohydrate** 20 g (of which sugars 18 g), **fibre** 1 g

✓✓✓	C
✓✓	A, B$_6$, E
✓	B$_1$, folate, copper, iron, potassium

making more of vegetables

Beetroot raspberry smoothie

According to psychologists, we sense food with our eyes as well as our palates, and the colour and texture of dishes impart strong messages. The vibrant colour and luxuriously smooth texture of this vitamin-packed blend of beetroot, raspberries and cranberry juice make it irresistible.

Serves 4

2 cooked beetroot, about 125 g (4½ oz) in total, cooled and roughly chopped
55 g (2 oz) fresh or frozen raspberries
250 ml (8½ fl oz) cranberry juice drink, chilled
200 g (7 oz) Greek-style yogurt, chilled raspberries to decorate (optional)

Preparation time: 10 minutes

1 Put the beetroot and raspberries in a food processor or blender with the cranberry juice drink and purée until smooth.

2 Strain the purée through a nylon sieve into a large jug to remove the raspberry pips, then whisk in most of the yogurt.

3 Pour into 4 glasses and top with the remaining yogurt. Swirl the yogurt into the surface, then decorate with extra raspberries, if liked. Serve immediately.

Some more ideas

- For a refreshing cold soup, thin this drink down slightly with a little still mineral water.
- For extra kick, add a little hot horseradish sauce or some snipped fresh chives or chopped parsley or dill.
- Bought pre-boiled, vacuum-packed beetroot can be used for this recipe, but pickled beetroot preserved in vinegar is not suitable.
- To cook fresh beetroot, trim and wash, leaving them whole (skin, roots and leaf stalks in place). Place in a saucepan, cover with water and bring to the boil. Reduce the heat, cover and simmer for 20–40 minutes, depending on size, until tender. Drain, then cool under cold running water. Rub off the skin and drain the beetroot on kitchen paper.
- For a savoury beetroot-flavoured drink, purée a 5 cm (2 in) piece of cucumber (peeled or unpeeled, as preferred) with the beetroot, adding about 20 fresh mint leaves and 200 ml (7 fl oz) water. Add 100 g (3½ oz) Greek-style yogurt and 1–2 tbsp lemon juice, to taste. Garnish the glasses with cucumber slices and sprigs of mint.

Plus points

- Traditionally, beetroot was believed to be good for the health of the blood – probably because of its deep red colour. It does contain plenty of folate, which is essential for the formation of red blood cells as well as the proper development of the nervous system in unborn babies.
- The raspberries and cranberry juice drink provide vitamin C; raspberries also contain B-group vitamins.
- Cranberry juice contains a compound that helps to prevent *E. coli* bacteria from causing bladder and urinary-tract infections.

Each serving provides Ⓥ

kcal 100, **protein** 5 g, **fat** 5 g (of which saturated fat 3 g), **carbohydrate** 10 g (of which sugars 10 g), **fibre** 1 g

✓✓✓	C
✓✓	folate
✓	B_2, calcium, potassium

making more of vegetables

Red pepper pick-me-up

Drinking fresh vegetable and fruit juices is one of the easiest ways to add vitamins and minerals to your diet. Vegetables are particularly versatile because they can be used both in sweet drinks and in savoury, even spicy, mixtures for sophisticated cocktails. Serve this bright example at any time of day for an instant lift.

Serves 2
1 large red pepper
200 ml (7 fl oz) tomato juice
4 celery sticks, coarsely chopped
dash of Tabasco sauce
To serve
ice cubes
paprika
celery leaves to garnish (optional)

Preparation time: 20 minutes, plus
    15 minutes standing

1 Preheat the grill to the hottest setting. Grill the pepper for about 10 minutes, turning often, until the skin is charred on all sides. Place the pepper in a polythene bag and leave to stand for 15 minutes or until it is cool enough to handle.

2 Peel off the skin, then cut the pepper in half and discard the seeds, the white ribs of pith and the stalk. Cut the flesh into chunks.

3 Put the pepper, tomato juice and celery in a blender or food processor and purée until smooth. For a very smooth result, press the drink through a sieve. Stir in the Tabasco.

4 Pour the drink into 2 large glasses and add a few ice cubes. Sprinkle the top of each with a pinch of paprika and garnish with celery leaves, if you wish. Serve immediately.

Some more ideas

● For a fruity beetroot and celery drink, coarsely grate 1 raw beetroot and slice 2 celery sticks, then blend these with the grated zest and juice of 1 orange and 150 ml (5 fl oz) apple juice. Add a pinch of ground cinnamon and serve in glasses over ice cubes.

● For a carrot, ginger and orange pick-me-up, coarsely chop 2 dessert apples, cored, and 2 oranges, peeled, discarding the pips from the oranges, then purée with ½ tsp grated fresh root ginger and 500 ml (17 fl oz) carrot juice.

Plus points

● The vitamin content of this drink easily justifies its title as a pick-me-up. Red peppers are an excellent source of both beta-carotene (which is an antioxidant in its own right and which the body converts into vitamin A) and vitamin C. The tomato juice also provides vitamin C.

● Celery provides potassium. In addition, it is a natural diuretic, helping to reduce fluid and salt retention, and is therefore an aid in treating high blood pressure.

Each serving provides Ⓥ
kcal 45, **protein** 2 g, **fat** 0.5 g (of which saturated fat 0.1 g), **carbohydrate** 9 g (of which sugars 8 g), **fibre** 3 g

✓✓✓	A, C
✓✓	E
✓	B$_6$, folate, niacin, potassium

making more of vegetables

Crudités with three dips

Few foods can be healthier than raw vegetable sticks, so make the most of them by serving them with tempting low-fat dips for a snack or instead of a formal first course. Or, for a light lunch, these quantities will serve 4. You could also offer a selection of fruit and warm pitta bread for dipping, as well as vegetables.

Serves 8

Pesto-yogurt dip

55 g (2 oz) fresh basil leaves

1 garlic clove, crushed

1 tbsp pine nuts

250 g (9 oz) plain low-fat bio yogurt

Fresh herb dip

170 g (6 oz) fromage frais

1 spring onion, finely chopped

2 tbsp finely chopped parsley

1 tbsp finely snipped fresh chives

1 tsp tarragon vinegar

Italian-style tomato dip

55 g (2 oz) sun-dried tomatoes (dry-packed)

85 g (3 oz) cottage cheese

85 g (3 oz) plain low-fat yogurt

30 g (1 oz) fresh basil leaves

salt and pepper

To serve

450 g (1 lb) mixed vegetable crudités, such as baby carrots, courgette sticks, baby sweetcorn (blanched in boiling water for 1 minute), green beans (blanched for 1 minute), pepper strips, chicory leaves and broccoli florets

Preparation time: 25 minutes, plus 30 minutes soaking

1 For the pesto-yogurt dip, use a pestle and mortar to crush the basil, garlic and pine nuts to a paste. Work in the yogurt a spoonful at a time, until thoroughly combined. Add seasoning to taste. Alternatively, purée all the ingredients together in a food processor or blender. Transfer to a bowl, cover and chill until required.

2 For the fresh herb dip, stir all the ingredients together in a bowl until well blended. Cover tightly and chill until required.

3 For the Italian-style tomato dip, place the sun-dried tomatoes in a heatproof bowl and pour over boiling water to cover them. Leave to soak for about 30 minutes or until the tomatoes are plump and tender. Drain the tomatoes well, then pat them dry and finely chop them.

4 Purée the cottage cheese with the yogurt in a food processor or blender. Alternatively, press the cheese through a sieve and stir in the yogurt. Transfer to a bowl and stir in the tomatoes. Cover and chill until required.

5 Just before serving the Italian-style tomato dip, finely shred the basil and stir in with seasoning to taste.

6 Serve the bowls of dips on a large platter with the crudités arranged around them.

Plus points

- Pine nuts are rich in a variety of minerals: magnesium, potassium, iron, zinc and copper.
- Dairy products such as yogurt, fromage frais and cottage cheese are valuable sources of calcium. This mineral is essential for the structure of bones and teeth, which contain 99% of all calcium in the body.

Some more ideas

- There is a wide choice of vegetables for making crunchy, delicious crudités. For example, try celery or cucumber sticks, whole radishes, baby plum tomatoes halved lengthways, small cauliflower florets (raw or briefly cooked) and baby new potatoes cooked until tender.

Each serving (3 dips alone) provides Ⓥ

kcal 115, **protein** 6 g, **fat** 8 g (of which saturated fat 2 g), **carbohydrate** 6 g (of which sugars 5 g), **fibre** 0.5 g

✓✓	B$_{12}$, E
✓	B$_2$, calcium

making more of vegetables

making more of vegetables

Chunky vegetable soup

Although this is a hearty soup, laden with vegetables, it has a delicate flavour. Home-made stock is best, but you can use a good-quality bought stock (chilled or from a cube or powder); if using a cube or powder, do not add additional salt at the beginning of cooking as you may find these products provide enough salty seasoning.

Serves 4

1 tbsp sunflower oil

1 small onion, chopped

1 small leek, thinly sliced

1 large carrot, thinly sliced

1 bulb of fennel, sliced

225 g (8 oz) swede, cubed

225 g (8 oz) potato, peeled and cubed

1 bay leaf

several sprigs of fresh thyme

several sprigs of parsley

600 ml (1 pint) vegetable stock, preferably home-made (see page 28)

1 can chopped tomatoes, about 400 g

salt and pepper

fennel leaves (from the bulb, above) or snipped fresh chives to garnish

Preparation time: 15 minutes

Cooking time: about 1 hour

1 Heat the oil in a large saucepan. Add the onion and cook for about 5 minutes, stirring occasionally, or until softened but not browned.

2 Add the leek, carrot, fennel, swede and potato, and cook for a further 5 minutes or until slightly softened. Tie the bay leaf, thyme and parsley sprigs together into a bouquet garni. Add to the pan, together with the stock and tomatoes with their juice. Season to taste and bring to the boil, then cover the pan and reduce the heat. Simmer gently for 45 minutes or until all the vegetables are tender.

3 Remove the bouquet garni and check the seasoning. Sprinkle the soup with snipped fennel leaves or chives and serve piping hot. Mixed-grain or wholemeal bread are delicious with this soup.

Plus points

• In these days of refrigerated transport and all-year-round variety, it is easy to forget the importance of traditional vegetables, such as swedes and potatoes, as a source of vitamin C. At one time, these roots were very important in preventing scurvy during winter months. Eaten frequently, they contribute a useful amount of vitamin C, the antioxidant properties of which are important in the prevention of cancer and heart disease.

Some more ideas

• For a hearty winter's chowder-type soup, simply add more vegetables. Try celeriac, turnips and parsnips. Shredded white or green cabbage is also good – add green cabbage halfway through the simmering. Cool and chill any leftovers and reheat them next day, when the soup will taste even better.

• Pearl barley is the traditional grain for soup in Britain and adds a delightful nutty texture. Stir 55 g (2 oz) pearl barley into the softened vegetables, just before the stock and tomatoes.

• Add 1 garlic clove, finely chopped, and 2 tsp caraway seeds with the onion.

Each serving provides (V)

kcal 130, **protein** 4 g, **fat** 4 g (of which saturated fat 1 g), **carbohydrate** 20 g (of which sugars 10 g), **fibre** 5 g

✓✓✓	A, C, E
✓✓	B₁, B₆, folate
✓	niacin, copper, iron, potassium

Carrot soup with orange

Thickening soup with potato gives a velvety smooth result without adding the fat used in other traditional methods. Served either hot or chilled, this soup is ideal as a dinner-party starter all through the year.

Serves 4

1 litre (1¾ pints) vegetable stock, preferably home-made (see page 28)

500 g (1 lb 2 oz) carrots, finely diced

100 g (3½ oz) potato, peeled and finely diced

100 g (3½ oz) leeks, chopped

2 strips of pared orange zest

4 tbsp orange juice, or to taste

salt and pepper

To garnish

4 tbsp single cream

2 tbsp coarsely chopped fresh flat-leaf parsley

1 strip of pared orange zest, cut into fine shreds

Preparation time: 15–20 minutes, plus cooling and 4 hours chilling if served cold

Cooking time: about 25 minutes

1 Pour the stock into a large saucepan and add the carrots, potato, leeks and orange zest. Bring to the boil over a high heat, skimming the surface as necessary, then reduce the heat to moderate and leave the soup to bubble for about 20 minutes or until all the vegetables are very tender.

2 Remove and discard the strips of orange zest. Purée the soup in a blender or food processor until smooth.

3 If serving the soup hot, return it to the rinsed-out saucepan. Reheat and add the orange juice, then adjust the seasoning. Ladle the soup into bowls and add a spoonful of cream to each, drizzling it over the surface. Sprinkle with the parsley and shredded orange zest and serve at once.

4 To serve the soup chilled, leave to cool, then chill for at least 4 hours. When ready to serve, stir in the orange juice, then adjust the seasoning. Garnish and serve as for the hot soup.

Plus points

• Making soup is an excellent way of preserving all the water-soluble vitamins – the B group and vitamin C – which are otherwise lost when the cooking water from vegetables is discarded.

• This low-fat soup is made with leeks instead of the usual onion. Leeks are a useful source of several water-soluble vitamins, including C and folate.

Some more ideas

• To make a filling broccoli soup, replace the carrots with 500 g (1 lb 2 oz) broccoli florets. Sprinkle each serving with a little grated nutmeg and top with about 1 tbsp crumbled blue cheese, such as Stilton.

• Make a green bean soup using this basic recipe. Replace the carrots with 450 g (1 lb) green beans, trimmed and chopped. Omit the orange zest and add 30 g (1 oz) finely chopped fennel, about ¼ bulb. Depending on the choice of beans, this soup may need sieving to remove fibres after puréeing the mixture – this is particularly important if using runner beans. Serve sprinkled with finely chopped fresh fennel leaves (from the bulb) or dill.

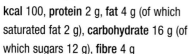

Each serving provides

kcal 100, **protein** 2 g, **fat** 4 g (of which saturated fat 2 g), **carbohydrate** 16 g (of which sugars 12 g), **fibre** 4 g

✓✓✓	A, E
✓✓	C
✓	B_1, B_6, folate, potassium

making more of vegetables

Asparagus and pea vichyssoise

Based on the classic leek and potato soup, this version has asparagus and sugarsnap peas added, and it is enriched with yogurt rather than cream for a lighter, lower-fat result. Traditionally served chilled, the soup can also be served hot, so it is ideal for days when the weather is changeable.

Serves 4

1 tbsp sunflower oil

170 g (6 oz) potato, peeled and diced

1 medium-sized leek or onion, coarsely
  chopped

300 g (10½ oz) asparagus, trimmed and
  chopped

200 g (7 oz) sugarsnap peas, chopped

1.2 litres (2 pints) vegetable stock, preferably
  home-made (see page 28)

1 tbsp finely snipped fresh chives or chopped
  fresh chervil

120 ml (4 fl oz) plain low-fat yogurt

salt and white pepper

snipped fresh chives or sprigs of fresh chervil
  to garnish

Preparation time: 10 minutes, plus at least
  1 hour chilling

Cooking time: about 20 minutes

1 Heat the oil in a large saucepan, add the potato and leek or onion, and stir well. Cover and cook over a low heat for 5 minutes, stirring occasionally, until the leek or onion has softened, but not browned.

2 Stir in the asparagus and sugarsnap peas, then pour in enough of the stock to cover the vegetables. Bring to the boil. Cover, reduce the heat and simmer gently for 5–7 minutes or until all the vegetables are tender.

3 Cool for a few minutes, then purée the vegetables with their cooking liquid in a blender or food processor. Pour into a bowl. Stir in the remaining stock, the chives or chervil and half of the yogurt. Season to taste with salt and white pepper. Leave to cool completely, then chill for at least 1 hour.

4 Taste and adjust the seasoning, if necessary. Ladle the soup into bowls and top each portion with a spoonful of the remaining yogurt. Garnish with chives or chervil and serve immediately, with rolls or crusty bread.

Plus points

● Asparagus is an excellent source of folate and it provides vitamins C and E as well as beta-carotene which is converted into vitamin A in the body. Asparagus also has a mild laxative effect.

● Sugarsnap peas provide good amounts of vitamin C and are a rich source of soluble fibre as they are eaten pods and all. This type of fibre helps to control levels of cholesterol and sugar in the blood.

Some more ideas

● To make a chilled cucumber soup, replace the asparagus and sugarsnap peas with 1 cucumber, chopped, and the chives or chervil with 1 tbsp very finely chopped fresh mint. Cucumber contains a lot of water so use only 600 ml (1 pint) of stock. Garnish with shreds of fresh mint.

● The soup freezes well, but do not add the yogurt before freezing: stir in the yogurt when the soup is thawed but still chilled, then season, garnish and serve as usual.

Each serving provides Ⓥ

kcal 140, **protein** 9 g, **fat** 4 g (of which
saturated fat 1 g), **carbohydrate** 20 g (of
which sugars 10 g), **fibre** 3 g

✓✓✓	C, E
✓✓	B$_1$, B$_2$, B$_6$, folate
✓	A, niacin, calcium, iron, potassium, zinc

Herbed cheese bagels

A little parsley adds a hint of freshness and colour to dishes, but when used in quantity its unique flavour can really be appreciated. It also makes a healthy contribution along with the vegetables to this delicious filling for bagels, which is based on creamy reduced-fat soft cheese.

Serves 4

100 g (3½ oz) reduced-fat soft cheese

2 spring onions, thinly sliced

30 g (1 oz) parsley, finely chopped

2 tbsp chopped fresh dill

1 tbsp chopped fresh tarragon

4 bagels

½ cucumber, thinly sliced

3 tomatoes, thinly sliced

1 red onion, thinly sliced

salt and pepper

Preparation time: 10 minutes

1 Put the soft cheese, spring onions, parsley, dill and tarragon in a bowl. Mix well together using a fork, then add seasoning to taste.

2 Slice the bagels in half horizontally. Spread the cheese mixture on the bagel bases. Layer the cucumber, tomato and onion slices on the cheese and cover with the tops of the bagels. Serve immediately.

Some more ideas

• After splitting the bagels in half, you can toast them lightly under the grill before adding the filling.

• For a mild herb flavour, reduce the quantity of parsley to 2 tbsp. Alternatively, for a peppery flavour, finely chop 1 bunch of watercress, tough stalks discarded, and use instead of parsley.

• Use 8 thick slices of Granary bread instead of the split bagels to make chunky sandwiches.

• For hearty open sandwiches, spread the herbed soft cheese on 4 individual or 2 large naan breads, cut across in half. Top with diced cucumber and sliced tomatoes (omit the red onion). Add a small handful of rocket leaves to each naan and scatter over 3–4 green olives, stoned and quartered. Fresh mint leaves can be used instead of rocket, if preferred.

Plus points

• Reduced-fat soft cheese is excellent for sandwiches as there is no need to spread the bagels or bread with butter – butter contains 5 times as much fat as the soft cheese, most of it saturated.

• Chunky sandwiches with vegetable fillings make well-balanced packed lunches and satisfying suppers. Large rolls, bagels, lengths of French bread or thick slices of a traditional loaf provide generous portions of starchy carbohydrate. Include plenty of vegetables or salad in the filling, with just a little protein-rich food such as meat, poultry, fish or dairy products.

• Parsley has long been appreciated as a breath freshener, particularly when eaten raw with or after a dish containing garlic. Parsley is a good source of folate, iron and vitamin C.

Each serving provides

kcal 170, **protein** 8 g, **fat** 5 g (of which saturated fat 2 g), **carbohydrate** 25 g (of which sugars 5 g), **fibre** 2 g

✓✓✓	C
✓✓	A, E, folate, calcium
✓	B_6, niacin, iron, potassium, selenium

making more of vegetables

Roasted vegetable baguettines

These Mediterranean-style 'sandwiches' are generously filled with char-grilled peppers, courgettes and red onion, spiked with garlic and rosemary, and topped with a sprinkling of feta cheese. They are real banquets in baguettes and far lower in fat than sandwiches with traditional fillings, such as Cheddar cheese and pickle.

Serves 4

2 red peppers, quartered lengthways and seeded

4 short French sticks or baguettines, about 125 g (4½ oz) each, halved horizontally

1 red onion, cut into small wedges

2 large courgettes, about 340 g (12 oz) in total, sliced diagonally

2–3 garlic cloves, chopped (optional)

3 sprigs of fresh rosemary

1 tbsp extra virgin olive oil

150 g (5½ oz) feta cheese

salt and pepper

Preparation time: about 45 minutes

Each serving provides ⓥ

kcal 500, **protein** 20 g, **fat** 14 g (of which saturated fat 6 g), **carbohydrate** 80 g (of which sugars 10 g), **fibre** 4 g

✓✓✓	A, C, folate
✓✓	B₁, B₆, B₁₂, niacin, calcium, iron, selenium
✓	B₂, copper, potassium, zinc

1 Preheat the grill to the hottest setting and grill the peppers, skin side up, for about 10 minutes or until the skins are blackened. Place the peppers in a polythene bag and set aside for 15 minutes or until they are cool enough to handle.

2 Meanwhile, lightly toast the cut sides of the French sticks under the grill. Remove the bread and set aside on a board.

3 Remove the grill rack and discard any crumbs from the bottom of the grill pan. Put the onion, courgettes and garlic, if using, in the grill pan. Sprinkle with the leaves from the rosemary sprigs and drizzle with the oil. Add seasoning, if required, and cook for 8–10 minutes, turning the vegetables once, or until browned on both sides.

4 Peel the skin off the peppers using a small sharp knife and cut them into thick slices. Arrange the peppers and courgette mixture over the bottom halves of the toasted bread, spooning all the pan juices from the courgettes over. Arrange side by side in the grill pan.

5 Crumble the feta cheese over the vegetables and grill for 3–4 minutes or until the cheese is slightly browned. Top with the remaining bread halves. Cut the baguettines in half at an angle and serve immediately.

Some more ideas

● For a picnic version, slice the top off an 18 cm (7 in) diameter small round white loaf. Scoop out the soft bread, leaving a shell about 2 cm (¾ in) thick. Brush the inside of the bread shell with 2 tbsp sun-dried tomato paste or black olive tapenade. Layer the cooled courgette mixture, peppers and 150 g (5½ oz) mozzarella, drained and thinly sliced, in the loaf. Replace the bread lid, wrap in cling film and chill. Cut into wedges to serve.

● For an easy-to-hold version, split the French sticks three-quarters of the way through, press flat like a book and toast lightly. Fill with the vegetables and feta and fold the bread closed. Serve immediately without grilling the feta.

● Drizzle a little balsamic vinegar over the grilled vegetable mixture before adding the feta.

● Fresh thyme can be used instead of rosemary.

● Use pitta breads or thickly sliced rye bread instead of baguettines.

Plus points

● Bread is an important part of a healthy diet as it is a complex carbohydrate, and also contributes fibre, vitamins and minerals, particularly calcium.

● Feta cheese is quite high in fat and salt, but because it has such a strong flavour, a little goes a long way.

making more of vegetables

Ciabatta with garlic mushrooms

Garlic mushrooms make a delightful starter, but classic recipes tend to use generous quantities of butter. This version, pepped up with mustard, is deliciously buttery without being over-indulgent. A simple salad of finely shredded white cabbage and chopped spring onion would be a good accompaniment.

Serves 4

1 part-baked ciabatta loaf
1 tbsp extra virgin olive oil
30 g (1 oz) unsalted butter
2 garlic cloves, crushed
450 g (1 lb) button mushrooms, halved
1 tbsp wholegrain mustard
dash of Worcestershire sauce
30 g (1 oz) Parmesan cheese shavings
salt and pepper
sprigs of fresh flat-leaf parsley to garnish

Preparation time: about 20 minutes

1 Preheat the oven to 200°C (400°F, gas mark 6). Cut the ciabatta diagonally into eight 2.5 cm (1 in) thick slices – they should be long and oval in shape. Place the slices of bread on a baking sheet and brush them lightly with oil. Bake the bread for 8–12 minutes or until crisp and golden.

2 Meanwhile, melt the butter in a frying pan. When the butter starts to sizzle, add the garlic and cook for 1 minute. Add the mushrooms and cook over a moderately high heat, stirring occasionally, for 4–5 minutes or until the mushrooms are lightly cooked.

3 Stir in the mustard. Reduce the heat slightly and add the Worcestershire sauce and seasoning to taste. Cook for a further 1 minute, then remove the pan from the heat.

4 Place 2 slices of ciabatta bread on each plate. Spoon the mushrooms and their cooking juices over the bread. Scatter on the Parmesan shavings and garnish with sprigs of parsley. Serve immediately.

Some more ideas

• Instead of part-baked ciabatta you can use part-baked French bread. Or, alternatively, use fully baked ciabatta or French bread and simply brush the slices with oil and toast under the grill.

• To make a roasted pepper bruschetta, preheat the grill to the hottest setting. Quarter and seed 2 red and 2 yellow peppers, then grill them, cut sides down, for about 10 minutes or until the skin is charred. Place the peppers in a polythene bag and set aside until cool enough to handle. Peel the skin off the peppers using a small sharp knife and coarsely chop them. Mix the peppers with 10 large fresh basil leaves in a bowl. Drizzle 2 tbsp balsamic vinegar and 3 tbsp extra virgin olive oil over the peppers and mix well. Divide the peppers and their dressing among the bread slices and serve immediately.

Plus points

• Mushrooms contain the water-soluble B vitamins B_2, niacin and B_6, all of which are important for the efficient metabolism of other nutrients. Mushrooms also contain copper, an essential component of many enzyme systems. Copper helps the body to absorb iron from food.

• The small quantity of Parmesan cheese here contributes useful calcium as well as a wonderful flavour.

Each serving provides

kcal 290, **protein** 11 g, **fat** 14 g (of which saturated fat 6 g), **carbohydrate** 34 g (of which sugars 2 g), **fibre** 2 g

✓✓✓	copper
✓✓	B_2, folate, niacin, selenium
✓	A, B_1, B_6, calcium, iron, potassium, zinc

making more of vegetables

Special savoury cornbread

Deliciously flavoured with sun-dried tomatoes, sweetcorn and green pepper, this colourful bread is a wonderful accompaniment for soups, starters, grilled or barbecued poultry or meat, or salads. It is also good cut into squares, split horizontally and filled with reduced-fat soft cheese and crunchy salad vegetables.

Makes 9 squares

55 g (2 oz) sun-dried tomatoes (dry-packed)
100 g (3½ oz) plain flour
100 g (3½ oz) fine cornmeal
1 tbsp baking powder
¼ tsp salt
1 large egg
200 ml (7 fl oz) semi-skimmed milk
3 tbsp corn oil
1 can creamed sweetcorn, about 200 g
1 small green pepper, seeded and finely diced
1 tbsp sesame seeds

Preparation time: 10 minutes, plus 30 minutes
    soaking and 15 minutes cooling
Cooking time: 25–30 minutes

Each square provides Ⓥ
kcal 200, **protein** 5 g, **fat** 10 g (of which
saturated fat 2 g), **carbohydrate** 25 g (of
which sugars 4 g), **fibre** 1 g

✓   B₁, B₁₂, C, niacin, calcium

1 Put the sun-dried tomatoes in a small heatproof bowl and pour boiling water over them. Set aside to soak for 30 minutes or until the tomatoes are plump and tender. Drain well and pat dry on kitchen paper, then snip into small pieces using kitchen scissors.

2 Preheat the oven to 220°C (425°F, gas mark 7). Grease an 18 cm (7 in) square deep cake tin and line the bottom with greaseproof paper; grease the paper. Set the tin aside.

3 In a large bowl, mix together the flour, cornmeal, baking powder and salt. In a separate bowl, lightly beat the egg, then stir in the milk, oil and sweetcorn until thoroughly combined. Pour the sweetcorn mixture into the dry ingredients. Add the sun-dried tomatoes and green pepper, and stir until well mixed. Pour the mixture into the prepared tin and sprinkle the sesame seeds over the top.

4 Bake for 25–30 minutes or until well risen and golden brown. Check that the bread is baked through by inserting a wooden cocktail stick into the centre – it should come out without any sticky mixture clinging to it. If there is mixture on the skewer, bake the bread for a further 5 minutes, then check again.

5 Allow the bread to cool in the tin for 15 minutes, then turn it out onto a wire rack. Serve warm or cold, cut into squares.

Some more ideas

● To make tasty savoury muffins, divide the mixture among 9 deep American-style muffin tins and bake for 18–20 minutes.

● For more crunch, replace the green pepper with 30 g (1 oz) roasted pumpkin seeds. Pumpkin seeds contain a lot of fat, but this is mostly the healthy, unsaturated type, and they also provide a variety of useful minerals.

Plus points

● In this recipe, 3 of the ingredients provide calcium, which is essential for healthy bones and teeth, nerves and blood clotting. Semi-skimmed milk is the most obvious source of calcium. Plain flour also provides some, but weight for weight the sesame seeds have the highest content. The calcium from milk is better absorbed by the body, however, than that in cereals and vegetables.

● Sweetcorn is a good source of the complex or starchy carbohydrate that health experts recommend.

making more of vegetables

52

Carrot bubble bread

Just pull apart the 'bubbles' or rolls to eat this delicious bread for brunch or as a healthy snack or accompaniment with a meal. The yeast dough is flavoured with a fresh carrot purée, and grated carrots and spring onions add more colour and crunch.

Makes 16 rolls or 'bubbles'

375 g (13 oz) carrots

400 g (14 oz) strong white (bread) flour

2 tsp salt

1 sachet easy-blend dried yeast

125 ml (4½ fl oz) semi-skimmed milk

1 tbsp extra virgin olive oil

about 150 g (5½ oz) strong wholemeal flour

4 spring onions, very finely sliced

1 egg, lightly beaten

Preparation time: about 45 minutes, plus about 3 hours rising

Cooking time: about 30 minutes

Each roll provides Ⓥ

kcal 140, **protein** 5 g, **fat** 2 g (of which saturated fat 0.5 g), **carbohydrate** 28 g (of which sugars 3 g), **fibre** 2 g

✓✓✓	A
✓	B₁, B₆, folate, niacin

1 Finely chop 250 g (9 oz) of the carrots and coarsely grate the remainder. Set the grated carrots aside. Cook the chopped carrots in the minimum of boiling water for 12–14 minutes or until soft. Drain and purée the cooked carrots in a food processor or blender, or mash them until smooth. Put the carrot purée in a sieve and press out as much moisture as possible, taking care not to press the carrots through the sieve. Leave the purée in the sieve to drain over a bowl.

2 Mix the white flour, salt and yeast in a bowl. Heat the milk with 125 ml (4½ fl oz) water until lukewarm. In a large bowl, mix together the carrot purée, the milk and water mixture and the oil. Stir in the white flour mixture to make a very soft dough. Gradually mix in the wholemeal flour to make a dough that will form a soft ball.

3 Knead the dough on a lightly floured surface for 10 minutes or until smooth but still soft and slightly moist. Lightly oil a large bowl and place the dough in it. Cover with cling film and set aside to rise in a warm place until doubled in volume (this will take about 2 hours).

4 Grease two 20 cm (8 in) round deep cake tins and line the bottoms with greased greaseproof paper. Knock back

the dough and knead for 2 minutes, then flatten it slightly. Sprinkle the grated carrots and spring onions over the top and continue kneading until they are well incorporated. If the carrots make the dough too moist, sprinkle it with a little extra flour and keep kneading until the flour is absorbed.

5 Cut the dough in half and cut each half into 8 equal pieces. Shape the pieces into smooth balls and arrange them in the prepared tins, one ball in the centre and the rest around the edge. Cover with a tea-towel (cling film may stick to the rolls when they rise) and set aside to rise for about 1 hour or until doubled in volume.

6 Preheat the oven to 200°C (400°F, gas mark 6). Brush the tops of the rolls very lightly with beaten egg, then bake for about 30 minutes or until golden. To test if the bread is cooked, tip it out of the tin and tap the base with your knuckles: the bread should sound hollow, like a drum. If not, continue baking for 5 minutes and then test the bread again.

7 Remove the bread from the tins and transfer to wire racks to cool. Serve warm or at room temperature. The bread can be kept in an airtight container for up to 2 days, or frozen for up to 3 months.

Some more ideas

- After dividing the risen dough in half, shape each piece into a free-form loaf on a lightly oiled baking tray, or put into two 450 g (1 lb) loaf tins. Leave to rise until doubled in volume, then bake as above.
- For a spinach bubble bread, cook and purée 400 g (14 oz) young spinach leaves, then squeeze out as much liquid as possible. Use this to make the dough instead of the carrot purée. Add 2 tbsp finely snipped fresh chives to the dough with the spring onions instead of the grated carrot.
- Add 2–3 tbsp finely chopped fresh herbs, such as parsley, sage, thyme or tarragon, with the vegetable purée (either carrot or spinach).

Plus points

- Carrots and wholemeal flour combine to ensure the bread provides plenty of fibre, important for control of blood levels of fats and sugars, as well as for healthy bowels.

Fruity vegetable muffins

Not only do grated vegetables and dried fruit add food value and flavour to these American-style muffins, but they also make them deliciously moist. Unlike many muffins, these are not too sweet, so they are as good in a packed lunch or as a snack as they are for breakfast or a tea-time treat.

Makes 12 muffins

125 g (4½ oz) self-raising flour
125 g (4½ oz) self-raising wholemeal flour
2 tsp ground cinnamon
170 g (6 oz) caster sugar
55 g (2 oz) dried mixed fruit or raisins
125 g (4½ oz) carrots, finely grated
125 g (4½ oz) courgettes, finely grated
125 ml (4½ fl oz) sunflower oil
3 eggs

Preparation time: about 15 minutes
Cooking time: 20–25 minutes

1 Preheat the oven to 180°C (350°F, gas mark 4). Grease a 12-cup deep muffin tin or line the cups with paper muffin cases; the cups should be about 3–3.5 cm (1¼–1¾ in) deep.

2 Sift both types of flour, the cinnamon and sugar into a mixing bowl, adding any bran left in the sieve. Stir in the dried mixed fruit or raisins, and make a well in the middle.

3 In another bowl, beat the carrots, courgettes, oil and eggs together. Pour this mixture into the well in the dry ingredients and stir until almost blended, but with a small amount of dry flour still visible in places.

4 Divide the mixture among the cups, filling them about two-thirds full. Bake for 20–25 minutes or until the muffins are well risen, peaked in the centre and springy to the touch. Transfer the muffins to a wire rack to cool.

5 Serve the muffins warm or at room temperature. They are best eaten on the day they are made, but they can be stored in an airtight container for up to 2 days. Alternatively, freeze them for up to 3 months.

Plus points

● The dried fruit in the muffins provides iron. For a healthy breakfast, serve fresh orange juice with the muffins – the vitamin C from the orange juice will help the body to absorb the iron from the dried fruit.

● Combining wholemeal flour with white flour increases the fibre content of baked goods without making them too heavy.

Some more ideas

● Replace the carrots with finely grated parsnips and add the grated zest of 1 lemon or orange.

● Children love chocolate muffins. To make a delicious, moist version with courgettes, sift 200 g (7 oz) self-raising flour, 170 g (6 oz) caster sugar, 45 g (1½ oz) cocoa powder and ½ tsp salt into a large bowl. Grate 250 g (9 oz) courgettes into another bowl and stir in 125 ml (4½ fl oz) sunflower oil, 3 eggs and 2 tsp pure vanilla extract. Stir the courgette mixture into the dry ingredients until well combined. Bake as in the main recipe.

Each muffin provides

kcal 260, **protein** 5 g, **fat** 13 g (of which saturated fat 2 g), **carbohydrate** 34 g (of which sugars 19 g), **fibre** 2 g

✓ A, B$_1$, B$_{12}$, niacin

Sweet pumpkin tartlets

Pumpkin is a good example of one of the many vegetables that can be used in both sweet and savoury recipes. Pumpkin pie is the best-known sweet preparation, and this is a lighter version made with filo instead of rich shortcrust and topped with fresh fruit. These tartlets are terrific with coffee or as a dessert.

Makes 8 tartlets

360 g (12½ oz) pumpkin flesh, about 450 g (1 lb) with peel and seeds

1 tbsp sunflower oil

15 g (½ oz) butter

3 eggs

1 carton reduced-fat evaporated milk, about 215 g

75 g (2½ oz) light muscovado sugar

4 tbsp desiccated coconut

grated zest and juice of 1 orange

½ tsp ground cinnamon

½ tsp ground ginger

½ tsp grated nutmeg

4 large sheets of filo pastry, 50 x 28 cm (20 x 11 in) each, about 140 g (5 oz) in total

To finish

100 g (3½ oz) blackberries or blueberries, or 2 ripe plums, stoned and thinly sliced

icing sugar

Preparation time: 35 minutes
Cooking time: 20–25 minutes

Each tartlet provides Ⓥ

kcal 180, **protein** 7 g, **fat** 9 g (of which saturated fat 3 g), **carbohydrate** 19 g (of which sugars 14 g), **fibre** 2 g

✓✓	A, B₁₂, E
✓	B₁, B₂, niacin, calcium

1 Cut the pumpkin into chunks and place in a saucepan. Add water to cover and bring to the boil, then reduce the heat and simmer for 20 minutes or until tender. Drain the pumpkin and return it to the pan. Replace the pan on the heat and mash the pumpkin with a potato masher until smooth. Continue heating for a further 4 minutes, stirring often, until most of the excess moisture has evaporated from the pumpkin. Set aside to cool.

2 Preheat the oven to 190°C (375°F, gas mark 5). In a small saucepan, warm the oil and butter together until the butter melts, then remove from the heat. Use a little of this oil and butter mixture to grease eight 7.5 cm (3 in) individual flan tins or Yorkshire pudding tins very lightly.

3 Whisk the eggs, evaporated milk, muscovado sugar, desiccated coconut, orange zest and juice, cinnamon, ginger and nutmeg together in a large bowl until well combined but not too frothy. Stir in the pumpkin purée, making sure it is evenly combined with the egg mixture.

4 Cut 32 squares measuring 12 cm (5 in) from the filo pastry – 8 squares from each sheet. Layer 4 filo squares in each prepared tin, brushing each square sparingly with the oil and butter mixture. Add the successive squares at different angles, so that the corners do not line up – they should create a pointed petal-edge effect.

5 Spoon the pumpkin filling into the pastry-lined tins. Bake the tartlets for 20–25 minutes or until the filling is lightly set. Allow to cool in the tins until warm.

6 Top the tartlets with blackberries, blueberries or plums and dust lightly with icing sugar, then serve immediately.

Plus points

● Pumpkin is a good source of beta-carotene, which the body can convert to vitamin A, and it also provides vitamin E.

● Pumpkin is easily digested, so is ideal for adding bulk to light desserts, and it is one of the foods that rarely causes allergies.

● Adding a fruit topping to desserts of this type is a good way of avoiding adding lashings of cream or other high-fat ingredients. Fresh fruit also has the advantage of contributing vitamins and fibre.

making more of vegetables

Some more ideas

- You can use 8 deep muffin tins instead of the Yorkshire pudding tins. The cooking time will be the same.
- Use butternut squash instead of pumpkin.
- Some sheets of filo pastry are smaller than those listed here. If using 31 x 18 cm (12½ x 7 in) sheets, you will need 11 sheets.

Cut out as many squares as possible, then overlap the trimmings to make up the layers.

- For a sweet potato and apple tart, cut 400 g (14 oz) sweet potato into chunks, then cook in boiling water for 15 minutes or until tender. Drain and mash as for the pumpkin. Omit the coconut and ginger, and add 1 dessert apple, peeled, cored and grated, and 55 g (2 oz)

raisins with the sweet potato purée. Layer six 50 x 28 cm (20 x 11 in) sheets of filo pastry in a deep 20 cm (8 in) flan tin or dish, brushing sparingly between the layers with the oil and butter mixture. Trim off excess pastry, leaving 1 cm (½ in) hanging over the rim. Pour in the filling and bake at 180ºC (350ºF, gas mark 4) for 35–40 minutes.

For Maximum Vitality

Tempting salads for all seasons

SALADS ARE A GREAT WAY TO BOOST daily portions of vegetables. Vary favourite salads with herbs and spices – try coriander and mint with tomatoes, or wholegrain mustard with mixed root vegetables in a creamy dressing. For a hearty supper, toss stir-fried cabbage with crisp celeriac, grapes and walnuts, and pile into baked potatoes. Or mix broccoli, courgettes and sugarsnaps with pearl barley. For a quick lunch combine toasted bread, cheese, crisp lettuce and tomatoes. Or start a party menu with an elegant salad of mixed leaves, mango and cashews.

Gold on a bed of green leaves

This mixture of salad leaves and herbs, each with its own robust flavour, marries well with the sweetness and smooth texture of mango. The result is a salad that is colourful and refreshing, ideal as a light starter or side dish. Serve with warm mixed-grain bread or rolls.

Serves 4

1 large ripe mango

200 g (7 oz) mixed baby spinach leaves, watercress and rocket or frisée

about 12 fresh basil leaves, coarsely shredded or torn

about 6 sprigs of fresh coriander, stalks discarded, then coarsely chopped

30 g (1 oz) cashew nuts or peanuts, toasted and coarsely chopped

Lime and ginger dressing

grated zest of 1 lime

2 tbsp lime juice

2 tsp finely chopped or grated fresh root ginger

1 tbsp toasted sesame oil

1 tbsp sunflower oil

salt and pepper

Preparation time: 15 minutes

Each serving provides Ⓥ

kcal 125, **protein** 3 g, **fat** 10 g (of which saturated fat 2 g), **carbohydrate** 6 g (of which sugars 3 g), **fibre** 2 g

✓✓✓	C
✓✓	A
✓	B₁, E, folate, calcium, copper, iron

1 Peel the mango. Cut the flesh from both sides of the stone and slice it thinly lengthways.

2 Mix the salad leaves on a platter, adding the basil and coriander. Arrange the mango slices on and between the salad leaves.

3 Whisk the ingredients for the dressing together and spoon it over the salad. Sprinkle with the chopped cashew nuts or peanuts and serve.

Some more ideas

• Thin strips of peeled cooked beetroot and cooked or raw celeriac are delicious additions to this salad.

• Instead of mango, use seedless green grapes, halved if large, thinly sliced dessert apple, or diced avocado.

• Toasted pumpkin seeds, sesame seeds or pine nuts can be used instead of the cashew nuts or peanuts.

• Replace the nuts with spicy croûtons. Cut 2 slices of day-old bread into small pieces or neat cubes and place in a polythene bag. Add a pinch of chilli powder and 1 tbsp extra virgin olive oil, then hold the bag shut and shake well. Tip into a non-stick pan and stir-fry until crisp and golden brown. Add to the salad just before serving.

• For a completely fat-free dressing, mix 1 tbsp seasoned rice vinegar (the type sold for making Japanese sushi) with the ginger and lime zest and juice. Add 2 tbsp fresh orange juice. Or mix 2 tbsp each of orange juice, dry sherry and soy sauce for a punchy dressing.

• A mixed green salad makes a versatile accompaniment for all meals or a useful base on which to serve ingredients such as fruit or smoked fish for a first course. Mix 225 g (8 oz) mixed salad leaves (cos, lamb's lettuce, Lollo Rosso, Little Gem, baby spinach or rocket) with about 45 g (1½ oz) mixed fresh herbs (basil, tarragon, chervil, flat-leaf parsley and mint), torn or coarsely chopped. Rub the inside of the salad bowl with a cut clove of garlic, if liked, then discard. Add the leaves and herbs to the bowl. For the dressing, whisk together 1 shallot, finely chopped, ½ tsp Dijon mustard, 2 tbsp white wine vinegar and 4 tbsp extra virgin olive oil with seasoning. Drizzle the dressing over the salad, then toss gently to coat the leaves.

Plus points

• Mango contains a wealth of carotenoids which protect against free radical attack and degenerative diseases. Mango also supplies iron, potassium, magnesium, and vitamins E, C and B group.

• All the leaves provide minerals, such as potassium, calcium and iron. Raw spinach provides folate. All these minerals help to protect against cancer.

Creamy root vegetable salad

It is easy to overlook root vegetables as a salad ingredient. Try this colourful mixture, tossed in a creamy, reduced-fat dressing, and discover a satisfying alternative to the ubiquitous mayonnaise-dressed potato salad. It makes a tempting light lunch or a delicious accompaniment to grilled meat or fish.

Serves 4

300 g (10½ oz) small new or salad potatoes, cut into 2.5 cm (1 in) cubes

200 g (7 oz) celeriac, cut into 1 cm (½ in) cubes

170 g (6 oz) swede, cut into 1 cm (½ in) cubes

200 g (7 oz) sweet potato, cut into 2.5 cm (1 in) cubes

juice of ½ lemon

Mustard and herb dressing

2 tbsp mayonnaise

2 tbsp plain low-fat yogurt

1 tsp wholegrain mustard

2 tbsp snipped fresh chives

1 tbsp chopped fresh dill

freshly ground black pepper

To finish

4 carrots, about 250 g (9 oz) in total

4 tbsp currants

3 tbsp pumpkin seeds

1 tbsp orange juice

1 tbsp extra virgin olive oil

To garnish

snipped fresh chives

chopped fresh dill

Preparation time: 45 minutes, plus cooling and 2–3 hours chilling

1 Place the potatoes, celeriac and swede in a saucepan. Add boiling water to cover and bring back to the boil. Reduce the heat and simmer for 10 minutes or until tender.

2 Meanwhile, place the sweet potato in another pan. Cover with boiling water, bring back to the boil and simmer for 3 minutes.

3 Make the dressing while the vegetables are cooking. Mix the mayonnaise, yogurt and mustard together. Stir in the chives, dill and black pepper to taste.

4 Drain all the vegetables well and put them in a large mixing bowl. Add the lemon juice and the dressing, and toss lightly. Set the vegetables aside to cool, then cover and chill them for 2–3 hours.

5 To finish the salad, use a vegetable peeler to cut ribbon strips from the carrots. Mix the carrot strips with the currants and pumpkin seeds. Stir in the orange juice and oil. Spread the carrot mixture in a large shallow serving bowl or place on individual plates.

6 Pile the chilled root vegetable salad on top of the carrot mixture. Garnish with a scattering of snipped chives and chopped dill, and serve.

Plus points

- Root vegetables are generally good sources of fibre, and starchy ones provide complex carbohydrate.
- Carrots offer vitamin A as beta-carotene, which is essential for good night vision.
- Pumpkin seeds are rich in fibre and minerals, such as iron, zinc and copper.

Some more ideas

- As an alternative to the carrot base, mix together 75 g (2½ oz) baby spinach leaves, 75 g (2½ oz) cos lettuce leaves, finely shredded, and 1 white onion, thinly sliced. Top with 75 g (2½ oz) sliced ready-to-eat dried apricots and 1 tbsp toasted sesame seeds, then sprinkle with the orange juice and oil.
- To vary the dressing for the root vegetables, replace the dill, chives and wholegrain mustard with 1 tbsp chopped fresh tarragon, 1 tbsp chopped parsley and 1 tsp Dijon mustard.

Each serving provides

kcal 350, protein 7 g, fat 15 g (of which saturated fat 2 g), carbohydrate 50 g (of which sugars 30 g), fibre 7 g

✓✓✓	A, C, E
✓✓	B₁, B₆, folate, potassium
✓	niacin, calcium, copper, iron, zinc

for maximum vitality

Radicchio and bean cups

Crisp, richly coloured radicchio leaves make the perfect edible holders for this tangy bean and mustard salad that is bursting with vitamins, minerals and fibre. Serve these salad cups as a substantial first course or, with plenty of fresh crusty bread, as a satisfying lunch or supper.

Serves 4

50 g (1¾ oz) thin green beans, trimmed and halved crossways

3 tbsp extra virgin olive oil

2 tsp wine vinegar

2 tsp wholegrain mustard

1 garlic clove, crushed

2 oranges

1 can red kidney beans, about 420 g, drained and rinsed

½ small red onion, finely chopped

30 g (1 oz) watercress sprigs, tough stalks discarded

50 g (1¾ oz) bresaola or German salami, cut into wide strips

4 large radicchio leaves

salt and pepper

Preparation time: about 20 minutes

1 Add the green beans to a small saucepan of boiling water and cook for 2 minutes. Drain, rinse under cold water and drain again, then set aside.

2 Mix together the oil, vinegar, mustard, garlic and seasoning to taste in a large bowl. Cut the peel and pith off the oranges. Holding the fruit over the bowl of dressing to catch any juice, cut the segments from between the membranes that separate them. Add the segments to the bowl. Squeeze the remaining juice from the membranes into the dressing before discarding.

3 Add the green beans, red kidney beans and onion to the dressing and toss together. Add the watercress with the bresaola or salami and toss lightly.

4 Place a radicchio leaf on each serving plate and fill with the bean mixture. Serve at once.

Some more ideas

• Canned mixed beans or lentils can be used instead of red kidney beans, or 100 g (3½ oz) dried Puy lentils. If using dried lentils, simmer in boiling water for 15–20 minutes, or according to the packet instructions, until just tender. Drain and rinse with cold water.

• For a main course, line a large dish with radicchio leaves and fill with the salad. Garnish with slices of orange.

• If making the salad for children, omit the mustard from the dressing and add 2 tsp tomato purée or ketchup instead. Use sliced lean cooked ham instead of bresaola or salami, and top with 55 g (2 oz) diced Cheddar cheese.

• Any variety of lettuce or a mixture of salad leaves can be used instead of the radicchio.

Plus points

• Green beans are a good source of fibre and they also provide valuable amounts of folate, a nutrient that is important before conception and in early pregnancy to ensure proper neural development of the baby.

• Oranges are an excellent source of vitamin C, with 1 orange providing more than twice the RNI of the vitamin. Studies have shown a connection between a regular intake of vitamin C and the maintenance of intellectual function in elderly people.

Each serving provides

kcal 290, **protein** 12 g, **fat** 15 g (of which saturated fat 1 g), **carbohydrate** 27 g (of which sugars 12 g), **fibre** 9 g

✓✓✓	C
✓✓	B₁, folate, iron
✓	B₆, E, niacin, calcium, potassium, selenium, zinc

for maximum vitality

Hot cabbage and grape coleslaw

Crunchy, lightly cooked white cabbage is perfectly complemented by juicy fruit, walnuts and herbs in this well-balanced salad. It is a good example of how a combination of familiar ingredients can be elevated into a sophisticated side dish. For a simple but delicious lunch or supper, serve the salad with baked potatoes.

Serves 4

200 g (7 oz) mixed salad leaves, including frisée

3 tbsp chopped fresh herbs, preferably chives, tarragon and parsley

1 tbsp walnut oil

1 tbsp extra virgin olive oil

125 g (4½ oz) celeriac

1 tbsp lemon juice

1 Asian pear

5 shallots, chopped

200 g (7 oz) white cabbage, finely shredded

4 tbsp red wine vinegar

125 g (4½ oz) seedless green grapes, halved

125 g (4½ oz) seedless red grapes, halved

45 g (1½ oz) walnut pieces

salt and pepper

Preparation time: about 25 minutes
Cooking time: 7–8 minutes

Each serving provides Ⓥ

kcal 215, **protein** 4 g, **fat** 14 g (of which saturated fat 1 g), **carbohydrate** 19 g (of which sugars 18 g), **fibre** 5 g

✓✓✓	C
✓✓	E, folate
✓	B₁, B₆, calcium, copper, iron, potassium

1 Combine the salad leaves with the herbs in a bowl. Add the walnut oil and 2 tsp of the olive oil and toss well. Arrange the dressed leaves on a serving platter or plates.

2 Peel the celeriac and cut it into matchstick strips. Toss with the lemon juice. Core the Asian pear and cut it into similar-sized strips. Toss with the celeriac and lemon juice, then scatter the celeriac and pear over the salad leaves.

3 Heat the remaining 1 tsp of olive oil in a large frying pan. Add the shallots and cook, stirring from time to time, for 4–5 minutes or until lightly browned. Add the cabbage and toss for 1 minute, then pour in the vinegar and boil for 1 minute or until the vinegar has reduced by about half. Add seasoning to taste and remove from the heat.

4 Add the green and red grapes and walnuts to the hot cabbage salad. Spoon the cabbage salad and its juices onto the dressed leaves, celeriac and pear, and serve immediately.

Some more ideas

• Use a firm, ripe dessert pear instead of the Asian pear.

• To make the salad into a light vegetarian lunch or supper dish, add 200 g (7 oz) smoked tofu, diced, with the white cabbage.

• For a main dish, add 200 g (7 oz) smoked chicken, cut into bite-sized chunks, with the cabbage. Serve with bread or potatoes.

Plus points

• Eaten in modest amounts, walnuts have a reputation for being a healthy food. This is because they contain the antioxidant nutrients selenium, zinc, copper and vitamin E, which protect against the cell damage that contributes to the development of cardiovascular disease and cancer.

• Cabbage belongs to a family of vegetables which contain a number of different phytochemicals that may help to protect against breast cancer. They are also good sources of vitamin C and among the richest vegetable sources of folate.

for maximum vitality

Mediterranean marinated salad

Inspired by Mediterranean cooking methods, this salad of roasted vegetables has a rich flavour cut by a piquant dressing. It is one of those any-time salads – ideal for a healthy mid-week meal with lots of crusty bread, some pasta or couscous; good as a dinner-party starter; or delicious with grilled fish, poultry or meat.

Serves 4

1 aubergine, cut into 1 cm (½ in) thick slices

1 red pepper, quartered lengthways and seeded

1 yellow pepper, quartered lengthways and seeded

4 baby courgettes, halved lengthways

2 tbsp extra virgin olive oil

1 garlic clove, crushed

4 canned anchovy fillets, drained and finely chopped

2 tbsp very finely chopped fresh rosemary

salt and pepper

sprigs of fresh rosemary to garnish (optional)

Honey mustard dressing

1 tbsp extra virgin olive oil

1 tbsp red wine vinegar

1 tsp runny honey

1 tsp Dijon mustard

Preparation time: about 1 hour, plus
    cooling and at least 4 hours marinating and
    1 hour resting

Each serving provides

kcal 140, **protein** 4 g, **fat** 10 g (of which saturated fat 1 g), **carbohydrate** 9 g (of which sugars 8 g), **fibre** 3 g

✓✓✓	C
✓✓	A, B$_6$, E, folate
✓	B$_{12}$, niacin, iron, potassium

1 Preheat the oven to 200°C (400°F, gas mark 6). Lay the aubergine slices in a single layer in a large roasting tin. Arrange the red and yellow peppers and courgettes around the aubergines, placing them cut sides up.

2 Brush the vegetables lightly with the oil. Scatter the garlic, anchovies and chopped rosemary over the vegetables, and add seasoning to taste. Roast the vegetables for 25–30 minutes.

3 Cover the vegetables with foil and roast for a further 10–15 minutes or until they are tender. Transfer the cooked vegetables to a large dish, layering them neatly, then drizzle the cooking juices over them.

4 Whisk the dressing ingredients together and pour over the vegetables. Cover and leave to cool completely, then put the vegetable salad in the fridge to marinate for at least 4 hours.

5 Remove the salad from the fridge 1 hour before serving so it can return to cool room temperature. Garnish with sprigs of rosemary, if you wish.

Plus points

- Aubergines are satisfyingly filling but low in calories – 100 g (3½ oz) contains just 15 kcal. They are renowned for absorbing oil when fried, but cooking them this way keeps the fat content very low.
- Rosemary is said to stimulate the nervous and circulatory systems, and soothe the digestive system.
- Courgettes provide vitamins B$_1$ and B$_6$.
- All of the vegetables in this dish are useful sources of fibre, and they provide lots of vitamins and minerals.

Some more ideas

- Replace the courgettes with 225 g (8 oz) plum tomatoes, halved, and use fresh thyme instead of rosemary. Roast the aubergines and peppers for 30 minutes, then add the tomatoes and roast for a further 15 minutes without covering with foil.
- For a vegetarian version, omit the anchovies and add 2 tbsp chopped capers instead.

for maximum vitality

Warm potato salad

Here tender new potatoes, cooked in their jackets, are combined with crunchy celery, spring onions and walnuts in a nutty dressing, then served warm. The salad is a delightful alternative to potato salads in creamy mayonnaise-based dressings, and goes well with cold meats or grilled fish, poultry, meat or vegetables.

Serves 4

450 g (1 lb) small new potatoes
50 g (1¾ oz) walnut pieces
3 celery sticks, thinly sliced
6 spring onions, thinly sliced
4 tbsp chopped parsley
sprigs of fresh flat-leaf parsley to garnish
Walnut balsamic dressing
2 tbsp walnut oil
1 tbsp balsamic vinegar
1 garlic clove, crushed (optional)
pinch of caster sugar
salt and pepper

Preparation time: 10–20 minutes
Cooking time: 20–25 minutes

1 Cut any large potatoes in half. Put the potatoes in a saucepan, cover with boiling water and bring back to the boil. Reduce the heat and simmer for 15–20 minutes or until the potatoes are just tender.

2 Meanwhile, make the dressing: whisk together the oil, vinegar, garlic, if using, sugar and seasoning.

3 Drain the potatoes and put them into a serving bowl. Add the walnuts, celery, spring onions and chopped parsley. Pour on the dressing and toss the ingredients together gently. Allow to cool slightly until just warm, then serve garnished with parsley.

Some more ideas

• Use Jerusalem artichokes instead of new potatoes. Peel or scrub the artichokes, as preferred, and immediately put them in a saucepan of water with a slice of lemon or a little lemon juice added to prevent them from discolouring. Cook as for the new potatoes.

• Add a peppery flavour with 55 g (2 oz) watercress or rocket leaves. Fresh coriander or basil can be used instead of parsley.

• Replace half the quantity of potatoes with an equal weight of other root vegetables, such as young carrots and/or baby turnips. Cook the carrots and turnips with the potatoes.

• Other oils can be used instead of walnut: try hazelnut, groundnut or pumpkin seed oil. For a creamy dressing, use 4 tbsp fromage frais instead of the oil.

Plus points

• Celery provides potassium, a mineral that is important for the regulation of fluid balance in the body, thus helping to prevent high blood pressure.

• Potatoes are a classic source of starchy carbohydrate for everyday meals. The preparation method makes a big difference to the amount of dietary fibre provided: new potatoes cooked in their skins offer one-third more fibre than peeled potatoes. Cooking potatoes in their skins also preserves the nutrients found just under the skin.

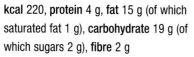

Each serving provides

kcal 220, **protein** 4 g, **fat** 15 g (of which saturated fat 1 g), **carbohydrate** 19 g (of which sugars 2 g), **fibre** 2 g

✓✓ B₆, C

✓ B₁, E, folate, copper, iron, potassium

Broccoli and pearl barley salad

Pearl barley, with its nutty flavour and firm texture, makes an interesting change from rice in grain-based salads, and it blends beautifully with this mixture of vegetables, sweet dried apricots and pumpkin seeds. Serve this as a satisfying lunch dish, adding some crumbled cheese such as feta for additional protein.

Serves 4

150 g (5½ oz) pearl barley

200 g (7 oz) broccoli, cut into small florets

3 courgettes, thickly sliced

100 g (3½ oz) sugarsnap peas, halved

55 g (2 oz) ready-to-eat dried apricots, thinly sliced

30 g (1 oz) pumpkin seeds

salt and pepper

Spicy tomato dressing

3 tbsp extra virgin olive oil

1 tbsp tomato purée

juice of 1 lime

2 tsp ground cumin

dash of Tabasco sauce

1 garlic clove, crushed

2 tbsp chopped fresh coriander or parsley (optional)

Preparation time: 50 minutes, plus cooling

Each serving provides

kcal 315, protein 10 g, fat 13 g (of which saturated fat 2 g), carbohydrate 42 g (of which sugars 9 g), fibre 4 g

✓✓✓	C
✓✓	B₁, E, folate, niacin, copper, iron
✓	A, B₂, B₆, calcium, potassium, zinc

1 Rinse the barley in one or two changes of water – do this in a bowl, swirling the grains with your fingers and pouring off the cloudy water. Drain the barley in a sieve, then place it in a saucepan and pour in 750 ml (1¼ pints) cold water. Bring to the boil, then reduce the heat and cover the pan. Simmer the barley very gently for about 30 minutes or until most of the water has been absorbed and the grains are tender but still firm. Drain the barley well.

2 While the barley is cooking, bring a second pan of water to the boil. Add the broccoli florets, courgettes and sugarsnap peas and bring back to the boil. Reduce the heat and simmer the vegetables for 3–4 minutes or until they are just tender but still crisp, then drain well and rinse briefly with cold water to refresh and stop the cooking.

3 Whisk all the dressing ingredients together in a large bowl. Stir in the apricots. Add the barley and vegetables as soon as they are cooked, and mix well to coat with the dressing. Check the seasoning, then cover and allow to cool until just warm.

4 Add the pumpkin seeds to the salad just before serving, warm or cold. Soda bread or wholemeal bread are good accompaniments.

Some more ideas

● Bulghur wheat can be used instead of pearl barley. Soak the bulghur wheat in plenty of cold water for 15 minutes, then drain thoroughly in a sieve. Tip the bulghur onto a clean tea-towel, gather up the towel around it and squeeze out excess moisture. The soaked bulghur does not need cooking.

● Use frozen vegetables instead of fresh – try one of the many mixtures available, such as frozen summer vegetables with peas, sweetcorn, red pepper and baby carrots. Cook in boiling water for 5 minutes, then drain well.

● Replace the pumpkin seeds with toasted sunflower seeds, or use coarsely chopped roasted peanuts or cashew nuts.

● Other grains to try in this salad include quinoa or buckwheat, both available from healthfood stores. Couscous is also suitable. Prepare according to the packet instructions.

Plus points

● Like other cereals, pearl barley is an excellent starchy carbohydrate. It is also low in fat.

● Broccoli is an excellent source of beta-carotene and vitamins C and E. It also provides B₆, folate and niacin.

● Dried apricots provide vitamin A (from beta-carotene).

for maximum vitality

Rustic bread and cheese salad

Inspired by the Italian salad called panzanella, *this combines crisp, garlic-flavoured bread cubes with sweet, juicy tomatoes and crunchy salad vegetables. Gruyère and Parmesan cheeses add wonderful flavour as well as vital minerals. Try it for lunch or supper, with more bread to boost the starchy carbohydrate.*

Serves 4

2 ciabatta rolls or 1 small baguette
2 garlic cloves, halved
1 egg, hard-boiled
1 tsp Dijon mustard
1 tbsp lemon juice
150 g (5½ oz) plain low-fat yogurt
75 g (2½ oz) Gruyère cheese
50 g (1¾ oz) Parmesan cheese
1 cos lettuce or 2 romaine lettuce hearts, cut into bite-sized chunks
2 beefsteak tomatoes or 4 plum tomatoes, skinned (optional) and cut into bite-sized chunks
1 bunch of spring onions, sliced
1 small bulb of fennel, thinly sliced
salt and pepper

Preparation time: about 20 minutes

Each serving provides ⓥ

kcal 265, protein 17 g, fat 13 g (of which saturated fat 7 g), carbohydrate 20 g (of which sugars 7 g), fibre 3 g

✓✓✓	C, calcium
✓✓	A, B₁₂, E, folate, niacin
✓	B₁, B₂, B₆, copper, iron, potassium, selenium, zinc

1 Preheat the grill. Slice the rolls or bread horizontally in half and toast both sides lightly under the grill. Rub the cut sides of the garlic over the toasted sides of the bread. Reserve the garlic cloves. Cut the bread into bite-sized cubes and set aside.

2 Separate the yolk and white of the hard-boiled egg. Roughly chop the white and set it aside. Mash the yolk with the mustard in a small bowl, then gradually stir in the lemon juice and yogurt, with seasoning to taste, to form a smooth dressing.

3 Using a cheese plane or vegetable peeler, cut fine shavings or very thin slices from the Gruyère and Parmesan cheeses. Alternatively, coarsely grate the cheese.

4 Rub the inside of a salad bowl with the reserved garlic cloves, then discard the garlic. Place the lettuce in the bowl and add the tomatoes, spring onions and fennel.

5 Add the dressing to the salad and toss lightly. Scatter over the egg white, bread cubes and cheese. Mix gently and serve at once, before the bread begins to soften.

Plus points

- The traditional combination of cheese and tomato offers a delicious source of protein, vitamins and minerals.
- In addition to calcium, Gruyère cheese is a good source of zinc, a mineral essential for the process of wound healing.
- Fennel is thought to aid digestion and relieve wind. It also provides phytoestrogen and it is a good source of potassium.

Some more ideas

- Use 1 head of Chinese leaves, about 400–450 g (14–16 oz), and 200 g (7 oz) iceberg lettuce instead of cos or romaine lettuce. Shred and mix the Chinese leaves and iceberg.
- Try 170 g (6 oz) feta cheese, crumbled, instead of Gruyère and Parmesan and add a few black olives, stoned and chopped. Omit the dressing and instead serve lemon wedges and black pepper to sprinkle over the salad.
- Grilled haloumi cheese is excellent with a salad such as this. Cut the cheese into fairly thick slices and place them on a flameproof dish. Cook under a hot grill until golden on both sides, turning once. Lay the cheese on individual portions of the prepared salad (made without Gruyère and Parmesan) and serve straightaway.

for maximum vitality

Zesty tomato salad

Seek out the most delicious tomatoes available, preferably sun-ripened on the vine, and you will be rewarded with an incomparable flavour. Lemon, fresh coriander and mint add freshness and zest to the tomatoes in this tangy salad, which can easily be varied with other fresh herbs and flavourings such as onion and garlic.

Serves 4

500 g (1 lb 2 oz) ripe tomatoes, sliced
pinch of caster sugar, or to taste
1 lemon
3 spring onions, thinly sliced
1 tbsp chopped fresh coriander
1 tbsp chopped fresh mint
sprigs of fresh mint to garnish

Preparation time: 10 minutes

1 Place the tomatoes in a large shallow dish and sprinkle with the sugar. Cut the lemon in half lengthways. Set one half aside, then cut the other half lengthways into 4 wedges. Holding the wedges firmly together on a board, skin side up, thinly slice them across, including the peel. Discard the pips.

2 Arrange the pieces of thinly sliced lemon over the top of the tomatoes, then sprinkle with the spring onions, coriander and mint. Squeeze the juice from the remaining lemon half and sprinkle it over the salad. Serve immediately or cover and chill until ready to serve. Garnish with sprigs of mint just before serving.

Some more ideas

• For a tomato salad with rosemary and basil, make a dressing by mixing together 1 tbsp each chopped fresh rosemary and basil, 1–2 garlic cloves, finely chopped, and 2 tsp raspberry vinegar or balsamic vinegar. Sprinkle the tomatoes with 3–4 pinches of sugar to emphasise their natural sweetness, and scatter over ½ red or white onion, thinly sliced. Sprinkle the dressing evenly over the tomatoes. Serve at once or cover and chill until ready to serve.

• A tomato salad makes a delicious filling for piping-hot baked potatoes, particularly baked sweet potatoes. Bake 4 large potatoes until crisp and golden outside and floury inside, then split and fill with the tomato salad. Top each potato with a spoonful of fromage frais or Greek-style yogurt and serve immediately.

• Tomato salads are good as omelette fillings. For each serving, make a plain omelette by lightly beating 2 eggs with 2 tbsp cold water and a little seasoning, then cooking in the minimum of olive oil in a very hot omelette pan until just set, lifting the edges to allow unset egg to run onto the hot pan. Spoon one-quarter of the tomato salad over half of the set omelette and fold the other half over. Slide the omelette onto a warmed plate. Serve with a mixed green salad and crusty bread.

Each serving provides Ⓥ

kcal 25, **protein** 1 g, **fat** 0.5 g (of which saturated fat 0.1 g), **carbohydrate** 4 g (of which sugars 3 g), **fibre** 1 g

✓✓✓	C
✓✓	E
✓	A, folate

Plus points

• Vitamin C, found in raw tomatoes, is an antioxidant that helps to protect against cancer. Tomatoes also contain lycopene, another valuable anti-cancer agent, believed to be particularly useful in protecting against prostate cancer. Lycopene is enhanced by cooking, so canned tomatoes, tomato purée or paste and tomato ketchup are better sources than fresh tomatoes.

for maximum vitality

Quick and Easy Main Dishes

Nourishing meals in just 30 minutes

MANY VEGETABLES NEED ONLY a few minutes to cook. Butternut squash, aubergine and courgette make a quick filling for tacos, topped with guacamole and a fresh tomato salsa. Frozen sweetcorn is good with potatoes and peppers in a fritatta, and peas go well with spinach and watercress in a sauce for tagliatelle. Broad beans are great with grilled poultry or delicious in risotto. For a healthy snack, grill peppers, passata and mozzarella, pizza-style, on a wholemeal bap. Or enjoy kebabs of new potatoes with mushrooms, patty pan squash and bacon.

Beef and mushroom Stroganoff

This version of the classic dish of quick-fried steak with mushrooms shows how vegetables can be used to enhance and 'stretch' a modest portion of meat. The result is every bit as special as true Stroganoff, and is more in keeping with today's taste for meals that are not dominated by meat.

Serves 4

2 tbsp extra virgin olive oil
200 g (7 oz) chestnut mushrooms, halved
1 red pepper, seeded and cut into fine strips
200 g (7 oz) broccoli, cut into small florets
150 ml (5 fl oz) beef stock
1 onion, sliced
300 g (10½ oz) fillet steak, cut into thin strips
2 tbsp brandy
3 tbsp creamed horseradish (optional)
150 ml (5 fl oz) soured cream
salt and pepper

Preparation time: 10 minutes
Cooking time: about 12 minutes

Each serving provides

kcal 370, **protein** 20 g, **fat** 29 g (of which saturated fat 14 g), **carbohydrate** 6 g (of which sugars 5 g), **fibre** 3 g

✓✓✓	A, B₁₂, C
✓✓	B₂, B₆, E, folate, copper, iron, zinc
✓	B₁, niacin, potassium, selenium

1 Heat half of the oil in a large saucepan. Add the mushrooms and fry for 2 minutes or until beginning to soften. Stir in the red pepper and broccoli florets and continue to fry, stirring, for 3–4 minutes.

2 Pour in the stock and bring to the boil. Cover the pan, reduce the heat and simmer for about 5 minutes or until the broccoli is just tender.

3 Meanwhile, heat the remaining 1 tbsp of oil in a large frying pan and stir-fry the onion for about 5 minutes or until softened and beginning to brown.

4 Add the strips of beef to the onions and stir-fry for 1 minute or until the beef begins to change colour. Stand back from the pan, pour in the brandy and set light to it.

5 As soon as the flames subside, stir in the creamed horseradish, if using, and the soured cream. Add the vegetables with their cooking liquid. Stir well, season to taste and serve immediately. A rice pilaff is the traditional Russian accompaniment for Stroganoff; tagliatelle is very popular today. Boiled new potatoes are also delicious with this vegetable-rich version.

Plus points

● Although not eaten in large quantities, horseradish contributes some fibre, B-group vitamins and vitamin C.
● Broccoli is a good source of vitamin C, which helps to increase the absorption of iron from the beef in this recipe.
● Mushrooms are low in fat and calories and they provide useful amounts of copper as well as many B vitamins.

Some more ideas

● Try lean gammon steak, cut into fine strips, instead of the fillet steak and replace the mushrooms and broccoli with 200 g (7 oz) white or green cabbage, shredded, and 150 g (5½ oz) frozen peas. Use vegetable stock instead of beef stock and cider instead of brandy (cider will not flame). Stir in 2 tbsp Dijon mustard (or your favourite mustard) instead of the creamed horseradish. Serve with light mashed potatoes (see page 29).
● Lean pork fillet or chicken or turkey breast fillets are good alternatives to the beef.
● For a vegetarian Stroganoff, omit the steak and use vegetable stock. Increase the quantity of mushrooms to 450 g (1 lb), including a variety such as open cap, shiitake and chestnut, and use 2 peppers.

Bacon and mushroom kebabs

In this dish, three favourite breakfast ingredients – bacon, mushrooms and tomatoes – are cooked on skewers with new potatoes and patty pan squash. The kebabs are served on toasted ciabatta with a refreshing citrus salad. Enjoy them for brunch at the weekend or as a mid-week supper.

Serves 4

1–2 tbsp extra virgin olive oil

grated zest of ½ orange

4 lean back bacon rashers, rinded

12 button mushrooms, about 125 g (4½ oz) in total

2 limes, quartered

12 cherry tomatoes

6 patty pan squash, halved, or 3 small courgettes, quartered

20 small new potatoes, about 500 g (1 lb 2 oz) in total, cooked

12 slices ciabatta or baguette

Citrus salad

1 pink grapefruit

1 bunch of watercress, thick stalks discarded

1 head of chicory, sliced

4 Agen prunes, pitted and sliced, or ready-to-eat dried apricots

2 tbsp chopped fresh mint

Preparation time: 15 minutes

Cooking time: 7–10 minutes

Each serving provides

kcal 580, protein 24 g, fat 13 g (of which saturated fat 3 g), carbohydrate 98 g (of which sugars 15 g), fibre 7 g

✓✓✓ B_1, B_6, C, folate, niacin

✓✓ calcium, copper, iron, potassium, selenium, zinc

✓ A, B_2, E

1 Place the oil in a small bowl and add the orange zest. Set aside to infuse while you make the salad.

2 Peel the grapefruit, removing all the pith. Holding the grapefruit over a large bowl to catch the juice, cut the segments from between the membranes that separate them, and drop them into the bowl. Squeeze the juice from the membrane before discarding it. Add the watercress, chicory, prunes and mint, and mix well. Set the salad aside.

3 Cut each bacon rasher into thirds by cutting off the thin end, then cutting the remaining piece in half lengthways. Wrap a piece of bacon around each mushroom.

4 Thread the lime quarters, bacon-wrapped mushrooms, tomatoes, squash or courgettes and cooked potatoes onto 8 metal skewers, dividing the ingredients equally between servings (2 skewers to each serving).

5 Preheat the grill to high. Brush the kebabs lightly with the orange-flavoured oil and cook under the grill for 7–10 minutes, turning once, until the bacon is golden brown and crisp.

6 Toast the slices of ciabatta or baguette on one side. Brush the untoasted sides lightly with the remaining orange-flavoured oil, then toast until lightly browned. Place on warmed serving plates. Add a pair of kebabs to each plate, laying them across the bread slices, and spoon the salad alongside. Serve immediately.

Some more ideas

• Replace the toasted ciabatta with couscous or rice tossed with finely chopped parsley.

• To make a meat-free version, omit the bacon. To add a vegetarian source of protein, use cubes of tofu instead of the mushrooms, and replace the tomatoes with 1 red pepper, seeded and cut into cubes. Make a basting sauce with the juice of 1 lime, 1 tsp honey, 1 tbsp light soy sauce, a pinch of cayenne pepper or chilli powder and a pinch of garlic salt. Serve with warm pitta bread and the citrus salad.

Plus points

• Bacon, like other meat, provides iron. Another bonus of both pork and bacon is that they have a high vitamin B_1 content. This vitamin is essential for maintaining a healthy nervous system.

• These kebabs provide excellent quantities of vitamin C from the grapefruit, tomatoes and potatoes.

Eggs with spicy peas and lentils

A little spice can turn a few everyday ingredients into something special. This simple, satisfying dish provides a wealth of vital vitamins and minerals and the right balance of essential protein and fibre. Serve with basmati rice and/or warm naan bread for plenty of energy-giving starchy carbohydrate.

Serves 4

1 tbsp sunflower oil

1 onion, chopped

2 garlic cloves, sliced

2.5 cm (1 in) piece of fresh root ginger, peeled and finely chopped

2 tbsp garam masala

1 tbsp tomato purée

450 g (1 lb) broccoli or cauliflower, or a mixture of the two, cut into small florets

450 ml (15 fl oz) vegetable stock, preferably home-made (see page 28)

55 g (2 oz) red lentils, rinsed

6 eggs

225 g (8 oz) frozen peas

3 tbsp chopped fresh coriander

coarsely grated zest of 1 lime (optional)

salt and pepper

To garnish

lime wedges

sprigs of fresh coriander

Preparation time: 10 minutes

Cooking time: 20 minutes

Each serving provides ⓥ

kcal 310, protein 24 g, fat 15 g (of which saturated fat 3 g), **carbohydrate 20 g** (of which sugars 6 g), **fibre 6 g**

✓✓✓	B_{12}, C, folate, iron
✓✓	A, B_1, B_2, B_6, E, niacin, copper, zinc
✓	calcium, potassium, selenium

1 Heat the oil in a saucepan and fry the onion, garlic and ginger for 3 minutes. Stir in the garam masala and tomato purée. Cook for 1 minute, then add the broccoli or cauliflower and seasoning to taste. Pour in the stock. Bring to the boil, then add the lentils. Cover the pan, reduce the heat and simmer for 15 minutes, stirring occasionally.

2 Meanwhile, put the eggs in a pan of cold water, bring just to the boil and boil gently for 6 minutes. Drain and rinse them under cold water, gently cracking the shells. Peel off the shells, taking care as the eggs will not be completely hard.

3 Add the eggs, whole, and the peas to the lentil mixture and stir gently. Bring back to simmering point, then cover the pan again and cook for about 5 minutes. By this time the peas should be cooked and the spicy sauce thickened with the softened lentils.

4 Remove the eggs with a spoon and cut them in half. Divide the spicy vegetable mixture among 4 plates. Mix the chopped coriander with the grated lime zest, if using, and sprinkle over the vegetables. Top each plate with 3 egg halves. Garnish with lime wedges and sprigs of coriander, and serve immediately.

Plus points

• The combination of spices in garam masala not only adds a distinctive flavour to Indian cooking, but has also been shown to possess natural preservative properties. These help to prevent bacterial growth in dishes that include it as an ingredient. (But foods should still be stored safely if they are not to be eaten immediately after cooking.)

Some more ideas

• This dish works well with frozen vegetables – mixed vegetables, broad beans, sweetcorn and green beans are all suitable.

• Replace the lentils with chickpeas. Drain 1 can chickpeas, about 400 g, and coarsely mash them, then add to the vegetable mixture in step 1. Reduce the quantity of stock to 300 ml (10 fl oz).

• A creamy sauce complements eggs. Try swirling 150 ml (5 fl oz) plain low-fat yogurt into the vegetable mixture once the eggs have been removed from the pan.

• Instead of adding boiled eggs, serve poached eggs on top of the spicy vegetable mixture.

Tamarind and cashew stir-fry

Once all the vegetables and the sauce have been prepared, this stir-fry can be cooked in minutes. It is an ideal quick mid-week meal, packed with ingredients that taste good and that are good for you too.

quick and easy main dishes

Serves 4

2 tbsp sunflower oil

55 g (2 oz) unsalted cashew nuts

200 g (7 oz) sugarsnap peas

200 g (7 oz) baby sweetcorn, halved

1 red pepper, seeded and cut into strips

200 g (7 oz) pak choy, sliced

Tamarind sauce

1 tbsp tamarind concentrate

2 tbsp light soy sauce

2.5 cm (1 in) piece of fresh root ginger, peeled and finely grated

1 tsp cornflour

2 tbsp dry sherry

To serve

400 g (14 oz) medium egg noodles

1 tsp toasted sesame oil

200 g (7 oz) bean sprouts

1 onion, thinly sliced

2 tbsp light soy sauce

2–3 tbsp chopped fresh coriander

Preparation time: 15 minutes

Cooking time: about 10 minutes

Each serving provides Ⓥ

kcal 615, **protein** 20 g, **fat** 20 g (of which saturated fat 4 g), **carbohydrate** 85 g (of which sugars 10 g), **fibre** 7 g

✓✓✓	B₁, C, E, folate
✓✓	A, B₆, niacin, copper, iron
✓	B₂, calcium, potassium, zinc

1 Mix the sauce ingredients with 2 tbsp of water in a small bowl, and set aside. Heat 1 tbsp of the sunflower oil in a wok or large frying pan and add the cashew nuts. Cook for 1 minute or until pale golden, then use a draining spoon to remove the nuts from the pan and set aside to drain on kitchen paper.

2 Add the sugarsnap peas, sweetcorn and red pepper to the wok and stir-fry over a high heat for 2–3 minutes or until the vegetables begin to soften. Pour in the prepared sauce and add the pak choy. Cook, stirring, for about 30 seconds, then cover and simmer for 2 minutes. Transfer the vegetables to a hot serving dish, scatter the nuts over and keep hot.

3 Cook the noodles in boiling water for 3 minutes. Drain, return to the pan and drizzle the sesame oil over them. Set aside.

4 Heat the remaining 1 tbsp of sunflower oil in the wok or frying pan and add the bean sprouts and onion. Stir-fry for 2 minutes. Add the noodles and cook for a further 3 minutes, tossing the ingredients together well.

5 Pour the soy sauce over the noodle mixture and transfer to a large serving dish or individual bowls. Sprinkle with the coriander. Serve the tamarind vegetables separately or pile them on top of the noodles.

Some more ideas

• For a Thai-style stir-fry, use mange-touts instead of sugarsnap peas, and replace the pak choy with 125 g (4½ oz) carrots, thinly sliced; 1 can sliced bamboo shoots, about 225 g, drained; and 4 spring onions, thinly sliced. Instead of the tamarind sauce, mix together 4 tbsp sweet chilli sauce, 2 tbsp light soy sauce, 1 tbsp Thai fish sauce and a 2.5 cm (1 in) piece of fresh root ginger, peeled and finely chopped. Serve with the noodle mixture or with plain boiled rice.

• Frozen vegetables make stir-fries even quicker to prepare. Try frozen sugarsnap peas, sweetcorn and green beans with chopped fresh spring onions, chopped garlic and/or chopped fresh root ginger. There is no need to thaw the vegetables first – just add them to a little hot sunflower oil and stir away.

• For a more substantial dish, add 200 g (7 oz) peeled raw tiger or king prawns with the sauce in step 2.

Plus points

• Cashew nuts offer vitamin B₁ and the minerals iron, zinc, magnesium and selenium. They also contain a high proportion of fat, but most of it is of the 'healthy' monounsaturated kind.

Speedy two-bean chilli

Here's a hearty and satisfying chilli – without the carne *(meat) – that can be made in minutes. This version combines two varieties of beans with sweetcorn in a rich tomato sauce flavoured with herbs, fresh chilli and chilli sauce. Serve with boiled rice or plenty of warm crusty bread.*

Serves 4

2 tbsp extra virgin olive oil

1 large onion, halved and sliced

1 fresh red chilli, seeded and chopped

1 can chopped tomatoes, about 400 g

1 tbsp chilli sauce

2 tbsp tomato ketchup

600 ml (1 pint) hot vegetable stock, preferably home-made (see page 28)

1 tbsp chopped parsley

1 tbsp chopped fresh oregano

1 can red kidney beans, about 400 g, drained and rinsed

1 can cannellini beans, about 400 g, drained and rinsed

200 g (7 oz) frozen sweetcorn

salt and pepper

To serve

150 g (5½ oz) fromage frais

2 tbsp snipped fresh chives

fresh oregano leaves to garnish

Preparation time: 5 minutes
Cooking time: 25 minutes

Each serving provides Ⓥ

kcal 385, **protein** 20 g, **fat** 10 g (of which saturated fat 3 g), **carbohydrate** 56 g (of which sugars 16 g), **fibre** 15 g

✓✓	B$_1$, B$_2$, B$_6$, B$_{12}$, C, E, folate, niacin, iron
✓	A, calcium, copper, potassium, selenium, zinc

---

1 Heat the oil in a large frying pan. Add the onion and chilli, and fry over a moderate heat for 5 minutes, stirring occasionally, until the onion is lightly browned.

2 Stir in the tomatoes with their juice, the chilli sauce, ketchup, stock, parsley and oregano, with seasoning to taste. Bring to the boil, then reduce the heat and simmer for 10 minutes, stirring occasionally.

3 Add the kidney and cannellini beans and the sweetcorn. Simmer for a further 10 minutes.

4 Meanwhile, mix the fromage frais with the snipped chives. Taste the chilli for seasoning and adjust if necessary. Serve the chilli sprinkled with the oregano leaves and offer the fromage frais mixture separately.

Some more ideas

● Serve the chilli with baked potatoes, with couscous or with warmed flour tortillas.

● Turn the bean mixture into vegetarian chilli burgers: cook the onion and chilli as in the main recipe, then place in a food processor. Omit the tomatoes and stock, but add all the remaining ingredients to the processor. Add 1 egg yolk and 200 g (7 oz) fresh breadcrumbs. Process until smooth, then divide into 8 portions. Shape into burgers and chill for at least 1 hour. Coat the burgers with more fresh breadcrumbs, pressing them on neatly – you will need about 75 g (2½ oz). Brush each burger with a little extra virgin olive oil and cook on a griddle or in a non-stick frying pan for 10 minutes on each side. Alternatively, cook under the grill preheated to moderate.

Plus points

● Pulses have a lot going for them. They are a cheap source of protein, a good source of B-group vitamins and, when sprouted, are an excellent source of vitamin C. In addition, kidney beans and cannellini beans provide more than 3 times the amount of fibre found in many vegetables.

Tacos with salsa and guacamole

Quick and easy to make, this filling and colourful main course is low in saturated fat but high in flavour. It is a great recipe to tempt even the most ardent of meat-eaters into enjoying a vegetable-based meal.

Serves 4

Aubergine and squash filling

2 tbsp extra virgin olive oil

1 onion, finely chopped

1 aubergine, about 280 g (10 oz), cubed

1 butternut squash, about 675 g (1½ lb), halved, seeded, peeled and cubed

1 large courgette, about 170 g (6 oz), cubed

¼ tsp chilli powder

½ tsp ground cumin

1 garlic clove, crushed

1 can tomatoes, about 400 g

salt and pepper

Guacamole

1 large ripe avocado

juice of ½ lime

Tomato salsa

3 ripe tomatoes, diced

½ red onion, finely chopped

4 tbsp chopped fresh coriander

To serve

8 taco shells, about 85 g (3 oz) in total

150 g (5½ oz) plain low-fat yogurt

pinch of paprika

lime wedges

sprigs of fresh coriander to garnish

Preparation time: 10 minutes

Cooking time: 20 minutes

1 Heat the oil in a large saucepan, add the onion and aubergine, and fry for 5 minutes over a high heat, stirring frequently, until the vegetables are lightly browned.

2 Add the butternut squash and courgette, then stir in the chilli powder, cumin and garlic. Pour in the canned tomatoes with their juice, and add seasoning to taste. Bring to the boil, breaking up the tomatoes with a wooden spoon. Cover the pan and simmer for about 15 minutes, stirring occasionally, until the squash is just tender. Check occasionally to ensure that there is enough liquid in the pan and add a little water, if necessary, to prevent the vegetables from sticking.

3 Meanwhile, preheat the oven to 180°C (350°F, gas mark 4). To make the guacamole, halve and stone the avocado, scoop out the flesh into a bowl and mash it with the lime juice. Mix together all the ingredients for the salsa in a separate bowl. Set the guacamole and salsa aside.

4 Put the taco shells on a baking tray and warm them in the oven for 3–4 minutes. Transfer the taco shells to warmed serving plates. Fill with the aubergine mixture. Top with guacamole, yogurt and salsa, then sprinkle with paprika. Garnish with lime wedges and coriander sprigs, and serve.

Plus points

- Avocados are high in calories, mainly from the monounsaturated fat they contain. This is the same type of fat that makes olive oil so highly recommended for the prevention of coronary heart disease. Avocados are also rich in vitamin E, an important antioxidant.
- When they were first introduced to Europe, tomatoes were the focus for suspicion, being known as love apples and thought to have aphrodisiac properties. We now know that they do have benefits for the heart, but not in the romantic sense.

Each serving provides Ⓥ

kcal 335, **protein** 9 g, **fat** 16 g (of which saturated fat 3 g), **carbohydrate** 40 g (of which sugars 19 g), fibre 8 g

✓✓✓	A, C, E
✓✓	folate, calcium, potassium
✓	B₁, B₂, B₆, niacin, copper, iron, zinc

Some more ideas

- This vegetable filling is also delicious rolled up in warmed flour tortillas. It will fill 8 tortillas, each about 15 cm (6 in) in diameter and weighing about 200 g (7 oz) in total.

- As an alternative to guacamole, put 1 can red kidney beans, about 215 g, drained and rinsed, in a food processor or blender with the juice of ½ lime; ½ small red onion, coarsely chopped; 1 tomato, chopped; 1 garlic clove, chopped; and 3 tbsp chopped fresh coriander. Whiz until creamy. Add seasoning to taste.

- Use quartered chestnut mushrooms in place of the courgette.

- If you do not want to heat the oven just for warming the taco shells, preheat the grill, then turn it off a few seconds before warming the taco shells in the hot grill compartment.

Potato, corn and pepper frittata

Known in Italy as frittata, or in Spain as tortilla, flat omelettes can be served hot or cold with salad for brunch, lunch or supper, and they also make ideal picnic fare. The delicious version here can be kept for a day in the refrigerator, but remove it about 30 minutes before serving as it tastes best at room temperature.

Serves 4

675 g (1½ lb) potatoes, peeled, quartered lengthways and thinly sliced across
1 red, yellow or orange pepper, seeded and chopped
2 tbsp extra virgin olive oil
1 onion, halved and thinly sliced
250 g (9 oz) frozen sweetcorn, thawed
6 eggs
4 tbsp finely chopped parsley
salt and pepper

Preparation time: 10 minutes
Cooking time: about 20 minutes

Each serving provides   Ⓥ

kcal 380, **protein** 18 g, **fat** 17 g (of which saturated fat 4 g), **carbohydrate** 42 g (of which sugars 4 g), **fibre** 4 g

✓✓✓	C
✓✓	B₁, B₆, B₁₂, E, iron
✓	A, B₂, niacin, copper, potassium, selenium, zinc

1 Put the potatoes in a saucepan, cover with boiling water and bring back to the boil. Reduce the heat, then add the chopped peppers and simmer for 3 minutes or until the potatoes are just starting to cook. Drain well, cover and keep hot.

2 Heat a 25 cm (10 in) non-stick frying pan over a high heat. Add the oil to the pan and swirl it around. When the oil is hot, reduce the heat to moderate, add the onion and fry, stirring often, for 3 minutes or until softened.

3 Add the potatoes, chopped pepper and sweetcorn and continue frying for about 8 minutes, stirring and turning the vegetables, until the potatoes are tender. Remove from the heat.

4 In a large bowl, beat the eggs with the parsley and seasoning to taste. Use a draining spoon to add the vegetables to the eggs, stirring them in thoroughly. (If any vegetables have stuck to the bottom of the pan, thoroughly clean and dry the pan before heating it with an additional 1 tbsp oil; however, this should not be necessary with a reliable non-stick pan.)

5 Replace the frying pan, with the oil remaining from cooking the vegetables, over a moderate heat. When the pan is hot, pour in the egg mixture, spreading out the vegetables evenly.

Cook the omelette, shaking the pan frequently, for 3–4 minutes or until the edges are set and the top is beginning to look set.

6 Meanwhile, preheat the grill to the hottest setting. Place the frittata under the grill for about 2 minutes or until the eggs are just set. Pierce the top of the mixture with a knife to check that the omelette is cooked through.

7 Remove the pan from under the grill and leave the frittata to set for 2 minutes, then slide it onto a serving plate. Serve hot or at room temperature, cut into wedges.

Plus points

• Sweetcorn is a useful source of dietary fibre – important for keeping the digestive system in good working order – and it also offers vitamins A, C and folate. Although some vitamins are lost in canned sweetcorn, they are retained in the frozen vegetable.

• Potatoes and peppers contribute vitamin C to this dish. In addition, potatoes offer starchy carbohydrates, which should make up at least half of the daily calorie intake in a healthy diet.

Some more ideas

● Take a tip from Spanish tapas bars and serve frittata at room temperature, cut into bite-sized pieces, as an alternative to salty or high-fat fried snacks with drinks.

● For a fennel and courgette frittata, replace the pepper, onion and sweetcorn with 1 bulb of fennel, thinly sliced; 85 g (3 oz) mushrooms, thinly sliced; and 1 courgette, cut in half lengthways and thinly sliced across. Fry these vegetables in the hot oil for 3 minutes before adding the part-cooked potatoes.

● For a simple pepper and potato frittata, use 3 peppers (any colour) and 2 onions, and omit the sweetcorn.

Tagliatelle with green sauce

This simple vegetable and yogurt sauce is ready in as little time as it takes to cook and drain the fresh pasta. It is bursting with fresh flavours and irresistibly creamy, but without the heaviness of a classic cream sauce for pasta. A salad of crisp radicchio and Lollo Rosso lettuce is a good accompaniment.

Serves 4

225 g (8 oz) baby spinach, thick stalks discarded

100 g (3½ oz) watercress, thick stalks discarded

125 g (4½ oz) frozen peas

500 g (1 lb 2 oz) fresh tagliatelle

2 tsp cornflour

200 ml (7 fl oz) Greek-style yogurt

4 tbsp chopped parsley

6 sprigs of fresh basil, torn into pieces

salt and pepper

Preparation time: 5 minutes
Cooking time: 7–8 minutes

1 Rinse the spinach and watercress and place in a large saucepan with just the water clinging to the leaves. Cover and cook over a moderate heat for 2 minutes, stirring and turning the vegetables occasionally, until they have wilted.

2 Add the peas and heat through, uncovered, for 2 minutes – there should be enough liquid in the pan to cook the peas. Tip the greens and their liquid into a bowl. Set aside.

3 Cook the pasta in a large saucepan of boiling water for 3 minutes, or according to the packet instructions, until al dente.

4 Meanwhile, blend the cornflour to a smooth paste with the yogurt, and put into the pan used for cooking the vegetables. Stir over a moderate heat until just bubbling. Add the vegetables, parsley, basil and seasoning to taste and stir well. Heat the sauce through, then remove the pan from the heat.

5 Drain the pasta and add to the sauce. Toss to mix with the sauce, then serve.

Some more ideas

• When fresh peas are in season, use them instead of frozen. Add to the spinach and watercress in step 1 and cook for 4 minutes.

• For a creamy broccoli and pea sauce, replace the spinach and watercress with 200 g (7 oz) broccoli. Cook the broccoli in a little boiling water for 5–8 minutes, then drain, refresh in cold running water, drain well again and return to the pan. Mash the broccoli with a potato masher, then add the yogurt mixed with the cornflour and 5 tbsp semi-skimmed milk. Stir in 125 g (4½ oz) frozen peas and 2 spring onions, finely chopped. Bring to the boil, stirring, and cook for 1–2 minutes to thicken. Season to taste and add a dash of lemon juice if you like. Toss with the freshly cooked pasta, then sprinkle with plenty of chopped parsley.

Each serving provides ⓥ

kcal 215, **protein** 11 g, **fat** 6 g (of which saturated fat 3 g), **carbohydrate** 30 g (of which sugars 3 g), **fibre** 4 g

✓✓✓	A
✓✓	C, E, folate, calcium
✓	B₂, niacin, copper, iron, zinc

Plus points

• Spinach and watercress are high on the list of foods that assist in the fight against cancer. They are also full of calcium and carotenoids and contain good amounts of vitamins E and C, and some B vitamins.

• Heat can destroy vitamin C. The best way to cook leafy green vegetables, such as spinach and watercress, and still retain the maximum vitamin C, is to wilt them briefly.

• Peas provide protein. They are also rich in fibre, some of it soluble, and this helps to keep blood sugar levels and cholesterol under control.

Sun-dried tomato and bean risotto

Moist risotto served with a simple side salad makes a satisfying carbohydrate-rich meal, and the risotto can be endlessly varied – all sorts of other vegetables (fresh, frozen, canned or dried) can be used instead of broad beans. To achieve the perfect texture, use risotto rice such as arborio and add the hot stock in stages.

Serves 4

1 tbsp extra virgin olive oil

1 large onion, chopped

2 garlic cloves, crushed

300 g (10½ oz) risotto rice

85 g (3 oz) sun-dried tomatoes (dry-packed), coarsely chopped

240 ml (8 fl oz) dry white wine

1.2 litres (2 pints) hot vegetable stock, preferably home-made (see page 28)

225 g (8 oz) frozen broad beans

55 g (2 oz) Parmesan cheese, freshly grated

30 g (1 oz) pine nuts

salt and pepper

12 large fresh basil leaves, freshly shredded, to garnish

Preparation time: 5 minutes
Cooking time: 25 minutes

Each serving provides Ⓥ

kcal 610, **protein** 17 g, **fat** 25 g (of which saturated fat 5 g), **carbohydrate** 67 g (of which sugars 5 g), **fibre** 4 g

✓✓	A, C, E, folate, niacin, calcium
✓	B₁, B₆, B₁₂, copper, potassium, zinc

1 Heat the oil in a large saucepan. Add the onion and garlic and fry over a moderate heat for 5 minutes, stirring frequently, until the onion softens and begins to colour.

2 Stir in the rice and sun-dried tomatoes, making sure the grains are coated in the oil, then pour in the wine. Bring to the boil, stirring occasionally.

3 Pour in half the hot stock and bring back to the boil, then reduce the heat and simmer, stirring frequently, for 10 minutes. Add the broad beans and half the remaining hot stock. Bring back to the boil again, then continue to simmer for about 10 minutes, adding the remaining stock in one or two stages as the rice absorbs the liquid.

4 The risotto is ready when the rice is tender but the grains are still whole, and the broad beans are cooked. It should be moist and creamy.

5 Add the Parmesan cheese and pine nuts with seasoning to taste and stir to mix. Serve at once, sprinkled with shredded basil.

Some more ideas

• To use fresh broad beans instead of frozen, allow 1 kg (2¼ lb) in pods. Shell them and add with the first batch of stock in step 3.

• Replace the broad beans with 300 g (10½ oz)

baby spinach leaves, stirring them into the cooked risotto just before the Parmesan cheese. This way, the spinach is freshly wilted and full flavoured when served.

• Add 3 tbsp pesto with the last of the stock and omit the Parmesan, pine nuts and basil.

• For a mushroom risotto, omit the broad beans and use chicken stock instead of vegetable stock. Add 1 tsp fresh thyme leaves with the first addition of stock. Just before the risotto has finished cooking, fry 450 g (1 lb) mixed fresh mushrooms, halved or sliced if large, in 30 g (1 oz) butter or 2 tbsp olive oil over a high heat for 3–4 minutes or until lightly browned. Stir the mushrooms and their juices into the risotto with the Parmesan. For an even richer mushroom flavour, add 1 tbsp finely chopped dried porcini mushrooms with the wine.

Plus points

• Rice is one of the most important staple crops, the very basis of life for millions of people worldwide. Polishing the grains to produce the familiar white varieties partially removes B vitamins; however, in this recipe, both broad beans and pine nuts provide B₁ and niacin.

• Along with other beans and pulses, broad beans are high in protein and low in fat, and offer good amounts of dietary fibre.

Quick bap pizzas

These are so simple and quick to prepare, yet they taste fantastic – almost as authentic as the real thing. They are ideal for a snack or a light meal with a fresh salad and some fruit to follow.

Makes 4 pizzas

1 large courgette, thinly sliced
1 yellow pepper, seeded and thinly sliced
1 tbsp extra virgin olive oil
2 large wholemeal baps, split open in half
120 ml (4 fl oz) passata with onion and garlic
handful of fresh oregano leaves
200 g (7 oz) mozzarella cheese, sliced
salt and pepper

Preparation time: about 5 minutes
Cooking time: about 10 minutes

1 Preheat the grill to the hottest setting. Line the grill pan with a piece of foil. Put the courgette and pepper slices on the foil, sprinkle with the olive oil and toss together. Spread out the vegetables, then grill for about 5 minutes or until they begin to soften.

2 Add the baps, laying them on top of the vegetables, crust sides uppermost, and toast lightly on the crust side. Remove the baps. Turn the vegetables and continue grilling them while you add the topping to the baps.

3 Spread the untoasted cut side of each bap with passata, allowing it to soak into the bread. Add a few oregano leaves to each one, then arrange the grilled vegetables on top, sprinkling them with seasoning to taste. Lay the slices of mozzarella cheese over the vegetables.

4 Put the bap pizzas back in the grill pan. Cook under the hot grill for 3–5 minutes or until the cheese melts and begins to brown. Serve immediately, while piping hot.

Each pizza provides Ⓥ
kcal 325, **protein** 20 g, **fat** 15 g (of which saturated fat 7 g), **carbohydrate** 30 g (of which sugars 7 g), **fibre** 5 g

✓✓✓	B₁₂, C
✓✓	A, B₁, B₂, E, folate, niacin, calcium, copper
✓	B₆, potassium, zinc

Plus points

● Peppers – green, yellow, red or other colours – are excellent sources of vitamin C, and red peppers are in a league of their own as a source of vitamin A from the beta-carotene they contain, providing 685 mg per 100 g (3½ oz).

● Cheese is a good source of protein and calcium, as well as many of the B vitamins. Mozzarella contains less fat than many other cheeses – in 100 g (3½ oz) there are 21 g fat and 289 kcal, compared to 34 g fat and 412 kcal in the same weight of Cheddar.

Some more ideas

● Use 6 patty pan squashes instead of the courgettes, and green pepper instead of the yellow pepper.

● Tuck some other fresh herbs, such as basil or marjoram, under the vegetables.

● For mushroom pizzas, use 300 g (10½ oz) sliced button mushrooms instead of the courgette and yellow pepper.

Extra Good Main Meals

Delicious vegetable-rich main dishes

BRING VEGETABLES TO THE HEART of the meal – for a healthy diet, reduce the meat in traditional dishes and add extra vegetables. Turnips and aubergines are delicious in lamb casserole. Eat vegetarian-style occasionally, too. Why not freeze a batch of veggie burgers for mid-week suppers? Mediterranean-style aubergine rolls in rich tomato sauce, topped with bubbling mozzarella, are rather special. Spring filo pie is just what it seems – crisp and light with tender vegetables. Or enjoy a cornucopia of vegetables in spicy sauce, served on fluffy couscous.

Celeriac dumplings in tomato broth

Fluffy white dumplings in a light tomato and vegetable broth make a delicious lunch or supper. The soup can be made in advance, and the dumplings can be shaped and chilled to be simmered just before serving.

Serves 4

1 red pepper

1 tbsp extra virgin olive oil

1 leek, thinly sliced

1 garlic clove, crushed

900 ml (1½ pints) vegetable stock, preferably home-made (see page 28)

1 tbsp tomato purée

140 g (5 oz) frozen petit pois

2 tomatoes, about 100 g (3½ oz) in total, skinned and roughly chopped

salt and pepper

sprigs of fresh basil to garnish

Celeriac dumplings

150 g (5½ oz) celeriac, diced, or 55 g (2 oz) cooked celeriac, mashed

75 g (2½ oz) fine fresh white breadcrumbs

125 g (4½ oz) soft mild goat's cheese

2 tsp chopped fresh basil

1 egg, beaten

Preparation time: about 1 hour, plus about 15 minutes cooling

Cooking time: about 20 minutes

Each serving provides Ⓥ

kcal 225, **protein** 12 g, **fat** 10 g (of which saturated fat 4 g), **carbohydrate** 22 g (of which sugars 7 g), **fibre** 3 g

✓✓	A, B₁₂, C, E, folate
✓	B₁, B₆, niacin, calcium, copper, iron, potassium, zinc

---

1 Preheat the grill to the hottest setting, then grill the red pepper for about 10 minutes, turning it often, until the skin is charred all over. Put it in a polythene bag and set aside until cool enough to handle. Peel the pepper, discard the seeds and cut the flesh into 1 cm (½ in) squares.

2 For the dumplings, cook the diced celeriac in boiling water for 10–15 minutes or until very tender. Drain well, then purée in a blender or food processor, or mash until smooth. Set aside to cool.

3 Meanwhile, heat the oil in a large saucepan. Add the leek and garlic, and cook for 1 minute. Stir in the red pepper, stock and tomato purée. Bring to the boil, then reduce the heat and simmer for 8 minutes. Add the peas halfway through the cooking. Remove from the heat. Stir in the tomatoes and seasoning to taste, then set aside.

4 Add the breadcrumbs, goat's cheese, basil and egg to the celeriac, with seasoning to taste. Mix well until all the ingredients are thoroughly combined. Use 2 small spoons (teaspoons are suitable) to shape the mixture into 12 small dumplings, setting them on a plate as they are made.

5 Bring a large saucepan of water to the boil. Gently lower half the dumplings, one by one, into the water on a draining spoon. Bring the water back to the boil, then cover, reduce the heat and simmer gently for 4–5 minutes. Use the draining spoon to remove the dumplings from the pan to a double layer of kitchen paper to drain. Repeat with the remaining dumplings.

6 Return the tomato broth to the heat and bring to the boil. Ladle the soup into bowls, add the dumplings and garnish with basil. Serve immediately.

Plus points

● Celeriac is related to celery and, like celery, it provides potassium. When eaten raw celeriac also offers vitamin C and soluble fibre, the type that helps to lower blood cholesterol levels.

● Goat's cheese is a tasty source of calcium. This complements the vitamins (C, A and B group), iron and protein from the vegetables in the soup to make a hearty one-dish meal.

Some more ideas

● For spinach dumplings, wash 200 g (7 oz) fresh spinach and place in a large saucepan. Cover and cook for 2 minutes or until wilted and tender – the water clinging to the leaves will provide sufficient moisture. Drain well, then press out all the liquid. Finely chop the spinach and use instead of the celeriac to make the dumplings. Add a good pinch of grated nutmeg to the mixture with the seasoning.

● Both the celeriac and spinach dumplings are delicious with a tomato sauce instead of soup. Cook 1 onion, finely chopped; 1 carrot, finely diced or chopped; 1 garlic clove, crushed; and 1 bay leaf in 1 tbsp extra virgin olive oil in a small saucepan for about 10 minutes or until softened. Add 2 tbsp tomato purée; 1 can chopped tomatoes, about 400 g; 200 ml (7 fl oz) vegetable stock, preferably home-made (see page 28); ½ tsp sugar; and seasoning to taste. Bring to the boil, then reduce the heat and cover the pan. Simmer for 15 minutes. Make and cook double the quantity of dumplings. Ladle the tomato sauce into 4 bowls, top with the dumplings and sprinkle with shredded fresh basil. A crisp salad is a good accompaniment.

Spinach pancakes with smoked trout and prawns

Spinach gives pancake batter a subtle flavour and added vegetable value, while mushrooms and peas complement the smoked fish and Cheddar filling. A tomato salad (see page 78) would complete the meal.

Serves 4

100 g (3½ oz) young spinach
125 g (4½ oz) plain flour
450 ml (15 fl oz) semi-skimmed milk
1 egg
generous pinch of grated nutmeg
about 1 tbsp sunflower oil
salt and pepper

Fish filling

30 g (1 oz) butter
125 g (4½ oz) mushrooms, sliced
300 g (10½ oz) frozen peas
50 g (1¾ oz) plain flour
600 ml (1 pint) semi-skimmed milk
150 g (5½ oz) peeled cooked prawns
125 g (4½ oz) smoked trout fillet, flaked
100 g (3½ oz) mature Cheddar cheese, grated
generous pinch of grated nutmeg

Preparation time: 15 minutes
Cooking time: 30 minutes

Each serving provides

kcal 615, **protein** 42 g, **fat** 27 g (of which saturated fat 14 g), **carbohydrate** 55 g (of which sugars 16 g), **fibre** 6 g

✓✓✓	B_{12}, folate, calcium
✓✓	A, B_1, B_2, B_6, C, E, niacin, copper, iron zinc
✓	potassium

1 Wash the spinach and place in a saucepan, then cover and cook for about 2 minutes or until wilted – the water on the leaves is enough moisture. Drain well, pressing out excess water.

2 Place the spinach in a food processor and add the flour, milk, egg and nutmeg. Season, then process to a smooth batter. (If you don't have a food processor, see 'Some more ideas'.)

3 Heat 1 tbsp oil in a 20 cm (8 in) non-stick frying pan, then pour out excess oil into a small bowl. Add enough batter to the pan to coat the bottom in a thin layer, tilting and swirling the hot pan as you do so. Cook for about 1 minute or until the pancake has set and is beginning to bubble, and the underside is lightly browned. Use a palette knife to loosen the edge of the pancake, then carefully turn it over and cook the other side.

4 Turn the pancake out onto a plate. Use the remaining batter to make 7 more pancakes, oiling the pan after every 2 pancakes, if necessary. Stack up the cooked pancakes on the plate as they are made, interleaving them with greaseproof paper. When all 8 pancakes are made, cover them with foil and keep them hot over a saucepan of hot water.

5 For the filling, melt the butter in a saucepan and add the mushrooms. Cook gently for 3 minutes, stirring. Add the peas and cook for 1 minute.

6 Whisk the flour into the milk until smooth, then pour this into the mushroom mixture. Bring to the boil, stirring, and simmer for 3 minutes. Stir in the prawns, trout, half of the cheese, the nutmeg and seasoning to taste.

7 Preheat the grill. Divide the filling among the pancakes, roll them up and place in a flameproof dish. Sprinkle the remaining cheese over and grill until golden. Serve immediately.

Plus points

● About one-third of the energy (calories) from trout is provided by fat, but only a small amount of this is saturated fat. Trout contains useful amounts of the fat-soluble vitamin E.

● Spinach, milk and cheese all provide calcium, adequate supplies of which are important throughout life for healthy bones and teeth. Adolescent girls in particular need a plentiful supply to protect against osteoporosis in later life.

Some more ideas

• If you do not have a food processor, sift the flour into a bowl, add the egg, nutmeg and seasoning, then gradually whisk in the milk. Finely chop the cooked spinach and stir it into the batter to mix evenly.

• Leeks and sweetcorn make a delicious vegetarian filling. Instead of the mushrooms, peas, prawns and trout, use 2 leeks, thinly sliced; 2 red peppers, seeded and thinly sliced; and 1 can sweetcorn, about 400 g, well drained. Add 2 tsp made English mustard to

the sauce, if liked, instead of the nutmeg.

• Replace the prawns and trout with smoked haddock. Poach 280 g (10 oz) smoked haddock fillet in gently simmering water for about 5 minutes or until just cooked. Drain, skin and flake the fish, discarding any bones.

Hotpot with golden parsnips

Middle-Eastern influences bring beans, aubergines, apricots, garlic and warm spices to this lamb hotpot, but the topping is in traditional British style – a golden layer of parsnip slices.

Serves 6

115 g (4 oz) dried black-eyed beans, soaked overnight

2 tbsp extra virgin olive oil

2 onions, sliced

1 garlic clove, chopped

500 g (1 lb 2 oz) boneless leg of lamb, cut into 2.5 cm (1 in) cubes

1 large aubergine, cubed

115 g (4 oz) ready-to-eat dried apricots, quartered

2 carrots, diced

225 g (8 oz) turnips, diced

½ tsp ground cinnamon

1 tsp ground cumin

1 tsp ground coriander

675 g (1½ lb) parsnips, thinly sliced

about 900 ml (1½ pints) vegetable stock, preferably home-made (see page 28)

salt and pepper

sprigs of fresh flat-leaf parsley to garnish

Preparation time: 30 minutes, plus overnight soaking

Cooking time: 1½ hours

Each serving provides

kcal 375, **protein** 25 g, **fat** 15 g (of which saturated fat 5 g), **carbohydrate** 38 g (of which sugars 19 g), **fibre** 10 g

✓✓✓	B₁₂
✓✓	A, B₁, C, E, folate, copper, iron, zinc
✓	B₆, niacin, calcium, potassium

1 Preheat the oven to 160°C (325°F, gas mark 3). Drain the soaked black-eyed beans and place them in a saucepan. Add cold water to cover, bring to the boil and boil rapidly for 10 minutes, then drain well. Set aside.

2 Reserve 1 tsp of the oil and heat the remainder in a large flameproof casserole. Add the onions and garlic, and cook for 2–3 minutes or until softened. Add the lamb and cook for about 5 minutes, stirring frequently, until browned. (If you do not have a suitable flameproof casserole, cook the onions and lamb in a frying pan, then transfer to an ovenproof dish. Bring the stock to the boil in the pan before pouring it into the dish.)

3 Stir in the aubergine, apricots, carrots, turnips, cinnamon, cumin and coriander, with seasoning to taste. Add the black-eyed beans and stir well.

4 Arrange the parsnip slices in a thick layer on top of the hotpot, slightly overlapping them, then pour in sufficient stock to come just below the surface of the parsnips. Bring to the boil, then cover the casserole and transfer to the oven. Cook for 1½ hours.

5 Preheat the grill. Brush the reserved 1 tsp of oil over the parsnips and place under the grill to crisp the top. Serve hot, garnished with parsley sprigs.

extra good main meals

Pork and spinach enchiladas

Much of the delight of Mexican food is in the abundance of salad-type toppings that contrast so well with the hot ingredients. Although these enchiladas are made with less fat than usual, their character is preserved, with chilli powder, cumin and paprika in the sauce and maize flour or corn tortillas used as thickening.

Serves 4

2 tsp extra virgin olive oil

115 g (4 oz) lean minced pork

1 onion, chopped

1 garlic clove, chopped

1 tbsp chilli powder, or to taste

1 tbsp paprika

1 tsp ground cumin

500 ml (17 fl oz) vegetable stock, preferably home-made (see page 28)

1½ tbsp *masa harina* (Mexican maize flour) or 1½ corn tortillas, toasted and crushed

2 tsp lemon or lime juice

12 corn tortillas

salt and pepper

4 tbsp fromage frais to serve

Spinach and cheese filling

750 g (1lb 10 oz) spinach

½ tsp ground cumin

3 spring onions, thinly sliced

340 g (12 oz) cottage cheese

30 g (1 oz) mozzarella cheese, finely diced

30 g (1 oz) Cheddar cheese, grated

Salad topping

3 spring onions, thinly sliced

4 tbsp chopped fresh coriander

1 Little Gem lettuce, shredded

15 radishes, diced

15 black olives, stoned and sliced

3 tomatoes, diced

Preparation time: 45 minutes

Cooking time: 15–20 minutes

1 Heat the oil in a wide saucepan and add the pork, onion and garlic. Cook, stirring, until the onion has softened slightly and the meat is lightly cooked.

2 Stir in the chilli powder, paprika and cumin. Cook for 1–2 minutes, then stir in the stock and bring to the boil. Reduce the heat and simmer for 10 minutes, stirring occasionally.

3 Mix the *masa harina* to a smooth paste with 4 tbsp water and stir into the sauce. Alternatively, stir the crushed toasted tortillas into the sauce. Bring to the boil, stirring, then reduce the heat again and simmer for 15 minutes. Add the lemon or lime juice and seasoning to taste. The sauce should be the consistency of single cream.

4 Preheat the oven to 200°C (400°F, gas mark 6). To make the filling, wash the spinach and place in a large saucepan, then cover and cook for about 2 minutes or until the leaves are wilted and tender – the water remaining on the leaves will provide sufficient moisture. Drain and cool, then press out excess moisture from the leaves and coarsely chop them.

5 Mix the spinach with the cumin, spring onions, cottage cheese and half of the mozzarella and Cheddar cheeses. Add seasoning to taste.

6 Bring the sauce back to a gentle simmer. Dip a tortilla into the simmering sauce for 30 seconds – just long enough to soften it. (Do not leave the tortilla in the sauce for too long or it may fall apart.) Lay the softened tortilla on a plate and top with a spoonful of the spinach filling. Roll up and place in a shallow ovenproof dish measuring about 38 x 25 cm (15 x 10 in). Repeat with the remaining tortillas and filling.

7 Pour the remaining sauce around the rolls – they should be about one-third submerged. Sprinkle the remaining mozzarella and Cheddar cheeses over the top. Bake for 15–20 minutes or until the enchiladas are hot and the cheese has melted.

8 Meanwhile, mix together all the ingredients for the salad topping. Serve the enchiladas topped with the salad. Drizzle the fromage frais over or offer it separately.

Each serving provides

kcal 645, **protein** 40 g, **fat** 16 g (of which saturated fat 4 g), **carbohydrate** 89 g (of which sugars 14 g), **fibre** 9 g

✓✓✓	A, B₁₂, C, E, calcium, iron
✓✓	B₁, B₂, B₆, niacin, potassium, zinc
✓	copper, selenium

Some more ideas

- Small flour tortillas can be used instead of the corn tortillas to make the enchiladas.
- Frozen chopped spinach can be used instead of fresh: thaw 500 g (1 lb 2 oz) and press out excess liquid.
- For a smoother filling, use ricotta cheese instead of cottage cheese. Alternatively, press the cottage cheese through a fine sieve.

- Shredded cabbage and Brussels sprouts are a delicious alternative to spinach in this filling. Shred 300 g (10½ oz) white or green cabbage and 15 Brussels sprouts, then blanch in boiling water for 3–4 minutes or until very lightly cooked. Drain the vegetables well.
- You can replace the pork with minced turkey or chicken. Use 1 tbsp olive oil for frying with the onion and garlic.

Plus points

- Although spinach contains a large amount of iron, this is not always easily absorbed by the body. The uncooked tomatoes and other ingredients in this dish supply vitamin C to aid iron absorption.

Winter vegetable casserole

Good food does not have to be complicated or time-consuming. This simple, homely casserole is made without a lengthy shopping list of exotic fresh ingredients or hours of precise slicing and chopping. Raid the storecupboard and use everyday vegetables from the refrigerator for a warming and heart-healthy meal.

Serves 4

2 onions, each cut into 6 wedges

3 carrots, cut into chunks

3 celery sticks, cut into chunks

400 g (14 oz) sweet potato or
　swede, cut into chunks

1 litre (1¾ pints) hot vegetable stock,
　preferably home-made (see page 28)

2 garlic cloves, finely chopped

3 leeks, about 300 g (10½ oz) in total,
　thickly sliced

150 g (5½ oz) pearl barley

2 tsp dried sage

salt and pepper

3 tbsp coarsely chopped fresh flat-leaf
　parsley to garnish

Preparation time: 15 minutes

Cooking time: 1 hour

Each serving provides ⓥ

kcal 205, **protein** 6 g, **fat** 2 g (of which saturated fat 0.1 g), **carbohydrate** 45 g (of which sugars 12 g), **fibre** 5 g

✓✓✓	A
✓✓	B₁, B₆, C, E, folate
✓	niacin, potassium

1 Preheat the oven to 180°C (350°F, gas mark 4). Put the onions, carrots, celery and sweet potato or swede in a large flameproof casserole. Pour in the stock and bring to the boil.

2 Add the garlic, leeks, pearl barley, sage and seasoning. Stir to mix the vegetables together. Cover and transfer to the oven to cook for about 1 hour or until the vegetables are just soft, and the barley is tender.

3 Sprinkle with the parsley and serve. Thick slices of farmhouse bread are an excellent accompaniment.

Some more ideas

• A combination of Puy lentils and barley works well in this casserole. Use 100 g (3½ oz) pearl barley with 55 g (2 oz) Puy lentils. After cooking for 30 minutes, add 1 Golden Delicious apple, cored and sliced, to the casserole. Sprinkle the finished casserole with 50 g (1¾ oz) hazelnuts, toasted and coarsely chopped, with the chopped parsley garnish.

• Other vegetables to add include parsnips, turnips and peeled chunks of butternut or kabocha squash.

• Use dry cider instead of the stock, and add 50 g (1¾ oz) ready-to-eat dried pears, chopped, for a hint of sweetness.

• The casserole can be simmered gently on the hob for 45–50 minutes, instead of cooking in the oven. Stir occasionally.

Plus points

• Barley is renowned for having a soothing effect on the intestines and urinary tract. It has long been considered a nourishing food for people convalescing after illness, and it is also beneficial for anyone suffering from stress or fatigue.

• Some gummy fibres present in the barley grain (beta-glucans) appear to have dramatic cholesterol-lowering ability.

• Root vegetables and leeks provide a wealth of fibre, vitamins and minerals.

• The ingredients are not fried as part of the first stage of preparing this casserole, so the result is low in fat. With some bread to accompany it, the meal also offers a healthy balance of starchy carbohydrates.

Stir-fried vegetable curry

A selection of ground and whole spices, and a hint of coconut, flavour the mixed vegetables in this contemporary curry, which is cooked in stages so that all the individual tastes remain distinct and delicious. Serve with boiled rice and naan bread or chapatis to make a substantial meal.

Serves 4

125 g (4½ oz) small pickling onions (unpeeled)

125 g (4½ oz) dried mung beans, soaked overnight, drained and rinsed

500 ml (17 fl oz) vegetable stock, preferably home-made (see page 28)

55 g (2 oz) creamed coconut, crumbled

1 tbsp finely chopped fresh root ginger

1 large garlic clove, crushed

1½ tbsp ground coriander

1 tbsp garam masala

½ tsp turmeric

pinch of crushed dried chillies

3 tbsp sunflower oil

1 tsp coriander seeds, crushed

1 tsp cumin seeds

1 tsp brown mustard seeds

250 g (9 oz) carrots, diced

250 g (9 oz) parsnips, diced

250 g (9 oz) small new potatoes, halved

250 g (9 oz) cauliflower, cut into small florets

150 g (5½ oz) frozen peas

125 g (4½ oz) white cabbage, shredded

salt and pepper

chopped fresh coriander to garnish (optional)

Preparation time: about 1 hour, plus overnight soaking

Cooking time: about 20 minutes

1 Blanch the pickling onions in a large pan of boiling water for 3 minutes. Use a draining spoon to remove them from the pan. Drain well and set aside until cool enough to handle, then peel.

2 Meanwhile, add the mung beans to the pan of boiling water and boil rapidly for 10 minutes, then reduce the heat and simmer for 20–25 minutes or until tender. Drain well and set aside.

3 Bring the stock to the boil, add the creamed coconut and stir until it dissolves. Set aside.

4 Using a pestle and mortar, pound the ginger and garlic to a paste. Stir in the ground coriander, garam masala, turmeric and chillies until well blended.

5 Heat a large wok or heavy-based flameproof casserole over a high heat. Add 2 tbsp of the oil. When the oil is hot, add the coriander, cumin and mustard seeds. Fry, stirring constantly, for about 30 seconds or until the seeds give off their aroma and start to crackle. Use a draining spoon to transfer the seeds to kitchen paper on a plate.

6 Add the remaining 1 tbsp of oil and the spice paste to the wok. Reduce the heat to moderate and stir-fry for about 1 minute. Stir in the carrots, parsnips, potatoes and 2 tbsp water, and stir-fry for a further 2 minutes.

7 Pour in the coconut stock and bring to the boil, stirring. Reduce the heat to low, cover and simmer for 5 minutes. Add the cauliflower florets, peas and pickling onions. Cover and continue simmering for a further 5 minutes, stirring occasionally. Uncover and bring back to the boil, then boil for about 5 minutes or until most of the liquid has evaporated and all of the vegetables are just tender.

8 Add the cabbage, mung beans and fried spice seeds, and stir-fry for just long enough to wilt the cabbage. Add seasoning to taste and serve immediately, sprinkled with chopped fresh coriander, if using.

Plus points

• Coconut features in many traditional curries, often in generous proportions. It is high in saturated fat, so here only a small amount is used to contribute flavour and body to the sauce.

• To preserve the vitamins under the skin of potatoes, just scrub them rather than peeling them before cooking.

• All the water-soluble vitamins (B group and C) from the vegetables are retained in the curry sauce.

extra good main meals

Some more ideas

● Courgettes, vegetable marrow and mushrooms can be used instead of the parsnips, peas and cabbage. Peel, seed and chop 600 g (1 lb 5 oz) marrow; coarsely chop 450 g (1 lb) courgettes; and cut 250 g (9 oz) button mushrooms in half. Add to the wok with the cauliflower and pickling onions.

● You can use hulled and split mung beans (called *moong dal* in India) rather than whole mung beans. The *dal* do not need to be soaked overnight, but will require 45–50 minutes cooking. Other alternatives are *toovar dal* and *urad dal* (a staple in the Punjab). Both of these split beans need to be simmered for about 1 hour to become tender.

Each serving provides

kcal 370, **protein** 11 g, **fat** 21 g (of which saturated fat 9 g), **carbohydrate** 37 g (of which sugars 16 g), **fibre** 9 g

✓✓✓	A, C, E, folate
✓✓	B₁, B₆, niacin, potassium
✓	copper, iron

Couscous Casablanca

Couscous is the staple food of much of North Africa, where it is often served topped with tender, colourful vegetables, drenched in delicious gravy and spiced with a traditional hot chilli sauce called harissa.

Serves 8

300 g (10½ oz) couscous

150 g (5½ oz) raisins

1 tsp ground cumin

2 tbsp chopped fresh coriander

1 tbsp lemon juice

chilli sauce to taste

pinch of ground cinnamon

1–2 tbsp orange flower water

Vegetable stew

3 tbsp extra virgin olive oil

2 large onions, chopped

4 garlic cloves, chopped

4 tsp ground cumin

1 tsp chilli powder

½ tsp each ground cinnamon, turmeric,
    cloves, coriander and ginger

1 can chopped tomatoes, about 400 g

1.5 litres (2¾ pints) vegetable stock,
    preferably home-made (see page 28)

225 g (8 oz) pumpkin, cut into chunks

1 small sweet potato, cut into chunks

2 celery sticks, sliced

1 carrot, cut into chunks

1 turnip, cut into chunks

100 g (3½ oz) runner or French beans, cut
    into short lengths

1 courgette, cut into chunks

1 can chickpeas, about 400 g, drained

salt and pepper

Preparation time: 40 minutes, plus 15 minutes
    standing
Cooking time: 35–40 minutes

1 To make the vegetable stew, heat the oil in a large saucepan or stockpot. Add the onions and half the garlic, and cook until they are slightly softened. Stir in the cumin, chilli powder, cinnamon, turmeric, cloves, coriander and ginger. Cook for a few seconds.

2 Add the tomatoes with their juice, the vegetable stock, pumpkin, sweet potato, celery, carrot, turnip and runner or French beans. Add seasoning to taste. Bring to the boil, then reduce the heat and simmer for 15–20 minutes or until the vegetables are just tender.

3 Stir in the courgette, chickpeas and remaining garlic. Cook for a further 15 minutes or until all the vegetables are quite tender. Traditionally, the vegetables for couscous are cooked until they are falling apart, but for a fresher result, cook only until the vegetables are tender and beginning to soften, but are not mushy.

4 Meanwhile, place the couscous and raisins in a large bowl. Add 250 ml (8½ fl oz) boiling water and mix well to moisten all the couscous. Set aside to soak for 5 minutes.

5 When the vegetables have finished cooking, ladle 500 ml (17 fl oz) of the hot liquid from them over the couscous. Cover and set aside to soak for 10 minutes. Cover the pan of vegetables and remove from the heat.

6 Meanwhile, make the harissa sauce. Ladle a further 175 ml (6 fl oz) hot cooking liquid from the vegetables into a bowl and stir in the ground cumin, chopped coriander and lemon juice. Add chilli sauce to taste.

7 To serve, reheat the vegetable stew, if necessary. Fluff up the couscous with a fork, then mound it on a platter or in a large bowl and sprinkle with the cinnamon and orange flower water.

8 Ladle some of the vegetable stew over the couscous and serve the rest separately. Serve the spicy harissa sauce on the side.

Plus points

• The mix of vegetables in this dish provides a nutritional bonanza as well as a delicious feast. Tomatoes supply vitamin C as well as the anti-cancer nutrient lycopene. Green beans offer fibre, and carrots are justly famous as a source of vitamin A (essential for good night vision) which occurs in them as beta-carotene, also beneficial as an antioxidant in itself.

• Couscous is low in fat and high in starchy carbohydrate.

Some more ideas

- Follow the seasons when choosing vegetables for the stew: French or runner beans, courgettes and pumpkin can be replaced by leafy greens such as curly kale or Brussels sprouts. Marrow is also a good candidate for well-flavoured dishes – add it instead of the pumpkin and courgette. Broad beans can be used as well as or instead of the chickpeas.
- Frozen vegetables are excellent in dishes like this one. Use fresh root vegetables as a base, then add frozen beans, peas and button Brussels sprouts.
- Add a large red, yellow or green pepper, seeded and coarsely chopped, with the onions and garlic in step 1.

Each serving provides ⓥ

kcal 315, **protein** 10 g, **fat** 6 g (of which saturated fat 1 g), **carbohydrate** 57 g (of which sugars 22 g), **fibre** 6 g

✓✓✓	A, C, E
✓✓	folate
✓	B₁, B₆, niacin, copper, iron, potassium

Potato and pumpkin gratin

When making a layered gratin such as this it's important to think about how the vegetables will cook, how much moisture they will release and whether or not they will hold their shape after cooking. A mixture of roots and softer vegetables yields a well-textured result and provides a good mix of nutrients.

Serves 4

450 g (1 lb) small main-crop potatoes, halved
600 g (1 lb 5 oz) pumpkin
150 ml (5 fl oz) dry cider
300 ml (10 fl oz) boiling vegetable stock, preferably home-made (see page 28)
1 small sprig of fresh rosemary
1 large red onion, halved and thinly sliced
3 beefsteak tomatoes, thickly sliced
2 sprigs of fresh oregano, stalks discarded
225 g (8 oz) Red Leicester cheese, grated
115 g (4 oz) fresh white breadcrumbs
salt and pepper

Preparation time: 45 minutes
Cooking time: 35–40 minutes

Each serving provides Ⓥ
kcal 480, **protein** 22 g, **fat** 20 g (of which saturated fat 12 g), **carbohydrate** 53 g (of which sugars 11 g), **fibre** 5 g

✓✓✓	A, C, E, calcium
✓✓	B₁, B₆, B₁₂, folate, niacin, potassium
✓	B₂, copper, iron, selenium, zinc

1 Preheat the oven to 180°C (350°F, gas mark 4). Put the potatoes in a medium-sized saucepan, cover with boiling water and bring back to the boil. Cook for 15 minutes or until they are just tender, then drain.

2 Meanwhile, prepare the pumpkin. Discard any seeds and fibres, then peel the flesh and cut it into 2.5 cm (1 in) cubes. Place in a saucepan and pour in the cider and stock. Add the rosemary. Bring to the boil, then partially cover the pan and simmer for 15 minutes. Add the onion and continue to cook for 10 minutes. Discard the rosemary and add seasoning to taste.

3 Slice the potatoes and arrange half of them over the bottom of a 2 litre (3½ pint) ovenproof dish. Lay half the tomato slices on the potatoes and scatter half the oregano leaves over. Season to taste with salt and pepper, and sprinkle with half of the cheese.

4 Spoon the cooked pumpkin on top, adding all the cooking liquid. Top with the remaining potatoes, tomatoes and oregano. Mix the remaining cheese with the breadcrumbs and sprinkle over the top of the vegetables.

5 Bake the vegetable gratin for 35–40 minutes or until the topping is crisp and golden brown. Serve piping hot with a crisp salad and crusty bread.

Some more ideas

• Replace the pumpkin with butternut squash or vegetable marrow.

• Use 225 g (8 oz) mushrooms instead of pumpkin, and omit the cider, stock, rosemary and onion. Halve or slice the mushrooms and mix them with 1 bunch of spring onions, chopped, then layer them in the gratin instead of the cooked pumpkin mixture. Increase the baking time to 45–50 minutes. The mushrooms give up their liquid during baking to moisten the gratin slightly.

• Instead of breadcrumbs, cut a loaf of ciabatta bread into small cubes and mix it with the cheese, then use this as a chunky topping.

Plus points

• This one-pot meal provides an excellent source of nutrients from many food groups. The vegetables supply plenty of fibre and a mixture of vitamins, including vitamin C from the potatoes and tomatoes, and vitamin A from the pumpkin (as beta-carotene). Cheese is an excellent source of calcium as well as protein. Bread is a good source of starchy carbohydrate and it also provides some protein and fibre. In addition, bread is fortified with calcium.

Stuffed baked potatoes

A steaming-hot baked potato makes perfect comfort food, and doesn't need lashings of butter and cheese to be delicious. This tasty vegetarian filling combines marinated mushrooms and courgettes, and there are 2 more satisfying fillings to choose from – tuna and sweetcorn, and roasted garlic and tomato.

Serves 4

4 baking potatoes, about 300 g (10½ oz) each

2 tbsp extra virgin olive oil

200 g (7 oz) small open-cup mushrooms, about 5 cm (2 in) in diameter

1 large courgette, about 170 g (6 oz), sliced

1 tsp red wine vinegar

1 tsp Dijon mustard

4 tbsp chopped parsley

salt and pepper

Preparation time: 15–20 minutes

Cooking time: 1¼ hours

Plus points

• Potatoes are an excellent source of vitamin C, especially when cooked in their jackets as the vitamin is stored just beneath the skin. A freshly dug potato may contain as much as ten times more vitamin C than one that has been stored.

Each serving provides Ⓥ

kcal 290, protein 8 g, fat 7 g (of which saturated fat 1 g), carbohydrate 53 g (of which sugars 3 g), fibre 5 g

✓✓✓	C
✓✓	B₁, B₆, folate, potassium
✓	A, E, niacin, copper, iron

1 Preheat the oven to 200ºC (400ºF, gas mark 6). Push a metal skewer through each potato or push the potatoes onto a potato roasting rack. (Pushing a metal skewer into the potatoes helps to conduct heat through to their centres so that they cook more quickly.) Place the potatoes directly on the shelf in the oven and bake for 1¼ hours or until they are tender.

2 Make the courgette and mushroom filling when you first put the potatoes in the oven so that it has time to marinate. Alternatively, it can be made just before the potatoes are cooked, and served hot. Heat a large ridged griddle or frying pan. Drizzle half the oil over the pan and cook the mushrooms and courgette slices for 10–15 minutes or until they are well browned in places and softened and have released their juices.

3 Transfer the vegetables to a bowl with all their juice and add the remaining oil, the vinegar and mustard. Season to taste, mix well and leave to marinate until the potatoes are cooked.

4 Split open the baked potatoes, then press gently to part the halves, keeping them joined at the base. Stir the parsley into the marinated vegetables, then pile them into the potatoes. Serve immediately.

Some more ideas

• To make a tuna and sweetcorn filling, put 225 g (8 oz) frozen sweetcorn in a small saucepan of boiling water. Bring back to the boil and cook for 2 minutes, then drain. Drain and flake 1 can tuna in water, about 200 g, and add to the sweetcorn. Stir in 2 tbsp mayonnaise and 2 tbsp reduced-fat crème fraîche. Mix in 2 tbsp snipped fresh chives or finely chopped spring onions and 2 tbsp chopped parsley, then pile the mixture into the baked potatoes.

• Roasted garlic and cherry tomatoes make a delicious filling. Trim the tough stalk off a whole bulb of garlic and wrap it in foil. Bake in the oven with the potatoes for 45 minutes. Cool the garlic slightly, then squeeze the pulp from each clove into a bowl. Add 1 large bunch of fresh basil, tough stalks discarded and leaves torn or shredded; 55 g (2 oz) stoned black olives, chopped; 1 tbsp extra virgin olive oil, and seasoning to taste. Stir in 450 g (1 lb) cherry tomatoes, quartered. Preheat the grill to a moderate setting. Scoop some flesh out of the potatoes, leaving a thick layer in the shells, and break the flesh up coarsely with a fork. Stir into the tomato mixture, then spoon the filling back into the potato shells and sprinkle with 55 g (2 oz) freshly grated Parmesan cheese. Brown under the grill and serve.

Risotto-filled acorn squash

Bring stuffed squash up to date with this risotto filling, richly flavoured with duck or chicken livers, red wine, garlic and sage. Full of iron and vitamins, duck and chicken livers are nutritious and surprisingly cheap freezer standby ingredients that are excellent for adding lots of flavour to vegetable and carbohydrate-based dishes.

Serves 4

2 acorn squash, about 675 g (1½ lb) each

200 g (7 oz) duck or chicken livers, thawed if frozen

2 tbsp extra virgin olive oil

1 onion, finely chopped

2 garlic cloves, crushed

170 g (6 oz) button mushrooms, thinly sliced

85 g (3 oz) risotto rice

200 ml (7 fl oz) vegetable stock, preferably home-made (see page 28)

200 ml (7 fl oz) red wine

2 tbsp chopped fresh sage

1 tbsp tomato purée

salt and pepper

To garnish

2 tomatoes, diced

fresh sage leaves

Preparation time: 25 minutes
Cooking time: 20 minutes

Each serving provides

kcal 365, **protein** 15 g, **fat** 8 g (of which saturated fat 1 g), **carbohydrate** 50 g (of which sugars 6 g), **fibre** 9 g

✓✓✓	B₁, B₂, B₆, B₁₂, C, niacin, folate, copper, iron
✓✓	A, E, potassium, zinc
✓	calcium

1 Cut the squashes in half lengthways. Trim a little off the base of each half so that it stands upright without wobbling. Discard the seeds and fibres, then scoop out the flesh to leave a shell about 1 cm (½ in) thick. Chop the squash flesh and set it aside.

2 Pat the livers dry on kitchen paper and coarsely chop them, discarding any white cores. Heat half the oil in a saucepan, add the livers and fry over a high heat for 2 minutes, stirring, until browned. Use a draining spoon to remove the livers from the pan and set them aside.

3 Add the remaining 1 tbsp of oil to the pan and fry the onion, garlic and mushrooms, stirring, for 3 minutes or until lightly browned. Stir in the rice, stock, wine, chopped sage, tomato purée and seasoning. Add the chopped squash. Bring to the boil, then reduce the heat and cover the pan. Simmer for 10–12 minutes, stirring occasionally, until the rice is tender.

4 Meanwhile, season the squash shells and place them cut sides down in a steamer. Cover and cook over boiling water for 10–12 minutes or until just tender.

5 Return the livers to the pan and stir them into the rice mixture. Cook for 2 minutes to reheat the livers.

6 Place the squash shells on serving plates and fill with the risotto. Garnish with the diced tomatoes and sage leaves, and serve. A refreshing salad of crisp radicchio and tomatoes goes well with this dish.

Plus points

• Low intake of iron and the anaemia that results are among the most common causes of nutritional problems in the UK. This dish provides iron from the livers and vitamin C from the acorn squash and tomato purée; the vitamin C helps to ensure that the iron is absorbed efficiently by the body.

• Acorn squash supplies vitamin A (from beta-carotene, the pigment that gives the squash flesh its rich colour).

• Rice is an ideal food to include in a healthy diet as it is a starchy carbohydrate and low in fat.

Some more ideas

• Use very finely chopped fresh rosemary leaves or 2 small bay leaves instead of the chopped sage. Discard the bay leaves before piling the risotto into the squash shells.

• Stuff 8 beefsteak tomatoes with the risotto. Cut a slice off the top of each tomato, scoop out the soft centre (use this in pasta sauces or casseroles) and place the tomato shells in a shallow ovenproof dish. Fill with the rice mixture and replace the tomato tops, then bake at 190ºC (375ºF, gas mark 5) for 12–15 minutes.

• The risotto also makes a delicious filling for red peppers. Cut the stalk ends off 4 large red peppers and scoop out the seeds. Steam the pepper shells in the same way as the squash shells, until tender. Fill, replace the pepper tops if you like, and serve piping hot.

• Replace the mushrooms with 170 g (6 oz) courgettes, diced, and 1 red pepper, seeded and diced.

Spicy red cabbage parcels

Eating well to feel good does not mean relying only on modern recipes for inspiration, as many more familiar dishes fit the bill perfectly. In this updated version of stuffed cabbage, mellow-flavoured red cabbage leaves are filled with a hearty mixture of turkey, lentils, rice and cashews and baked in a simple tomato sauce.

Serves 4

55 g (2 oz) long-grain rice
8 large red cabbage leaves
1 tbsp sunflower oil
1 onion, finely chopped
1½ tsp cumin seeds
1 tsp ground coriander
1 tsp ground cinnamon
3 tbsp mango chutney, chopped if necessary
45 g (1½ oz) salted cashew nuts, coarsely
    chopped
1 can green lentils, about 420 g, drained
100 g (3½ oz) cooked turkey or chicken,
    without skin, diced
4 tbsp chopped parsley
200 ml (7 fl oz) tomato juice
salt and pepper
sprigs of fresh flat-leaf parsley to garnish

Preparation time: 40 minutes
Cooking time: 30 minutes

Each serving provides

kcal 360, **protein** 22 g, **fat** 10 g (of which
saturated fat 2 g), **carbohydrate** 47 g (of
which sugars 17 g), **fibre** 6 g

✓✓✓ C, E

✓✓ B₆, folate, iron, copper, selenium

✓ B₁, niacin, potassium

1 Place the rice in a small saucepan. Pour in 300 ml (10 fl oz) of water and bring to the boil. Stir once, then reduce the heat to the lowest setting and cover the pan. Cook for 15 minutes. Remove from the heat and leave the rice to stand, without removing the lid, for 10 minutes.

2 Meanwhile, preheat the oven to 200°C (400°F, gas mark 6). Trim off the tough stalk from the base of each cabbage leaf. Bring a large saucepan of water to the boil. Add half the leaves, bring back to the boil and blanch for 30 seconds. Use a draining spoon to remove the leaves from the pan and plunge them into a large bowl of cold water to stop them cooking. Repeat with the remaining leaves. Drain the leaves well and leave to dry spread out on a clean tea-towel.

3 Heat the oil in a large pan and sauté the onion for 2–3 minutes or until softened. Add the cumin seeds and ground coriander and cinnamon, and cook for a further 2–3 minutes. Remove from the heat.

4 Add 2 tbsp of the mango chutney to the onion mixture together with the cashews, lentils, turkey or chicken, parsley and seasoning to taste, and mix well. Stir in the rice until thoroughly combined.

5 Lay a cabbage leaf flat on the work surface, with the stalk end towards you. Place some of the rice mixture on the leaf. Fold the base of the leaf over the filling, then fold in the sides and roll up the leaf to enclose the filling in a neat parcel. Repeat with the remaining leaves and filling.

6 Mix the remaining 1 tbsp of mango chutney with the tomato juice and seasoning to taste. Pour about one-quarter of this sauce into a large ovenproof dish. Pack the cabbage parcels into the dish and pour the rest of the sauce over them. Cover loosely with foil and bake for about 30 minutes or until the leaves are tender. Garnish with parsley and serve hot with a salad or vegetable accompaniment, such as lightly cooked sugarsnap peas.

Plus points

● Red cabbage provides useful amounts of the B vitamin folate and vitamin C as well as potassium. Potassium helps to protect against the adverse effects of a high salt intake on blood pressure.
● Turkey and chicken, without skin, are both first-class sources of low-fat protein.

Some more ideas

- Savoy or other green cabbage can be used in place of the red cabbage.
- For Chinese-style cabbage parcels, use blanched Chinese leaves instead of the red cabbage, and replace the lentils with 150 g (5½ oz) baby sweetcorn, sliced and cooked in boiling water for 4–5 minutes. Add 1 tbsp finely chopped fresh root ginger and 1 large garlic clove, crushed, to the onion. Use plum sauce instead of mango chutney and add 30 g (1 oz) toasted sesame seeds to the rice mixture. If preferred, peeled cooked prawns can be used instead of the turkey or chicken.

- Experiment with different types of rice: try basmati rice for its delicate flavour, or a mixture of wild rice and white rice. For more fibre, use brown rice – it requires longer to cook than white rice, so follow the packet instructions.
- Cooked ham or lean roast pork or beef can be used instead of the turkey or chicken.

Aubergine rolls

Unlike many aubergine recipes which swim in oil, this one has just enough extra virgin olive oil to enrich and enhance the vegetables in a dish that goes down well with both vegetarians and meat-eaters. This is a great cook-ahead dish, and it is delicious with crusty bread or baked potatoes and salad.

Serves 4

1 large aubergine, about 340 g (12 oz), cut lengthways into 10 slices, each about 3 mm (⅛ in) thick

2 tbsp extra virgin olive oil

1 onion, thinly sliced

4 garlic cloves, chopped

½ red pepper, seeded and cut into thin strips

½ green pepper, seeded and cut into thin strips

1 courgette, cut into thin strips

2 tbsp chopped parsley

6 tomatoes, diced

pinch of sugar

200 ml (7 fl oz) passata

4 tbsp chopped fresh basil

170 g (6 oz) mozzarella cheese, diced

8 black olives, stoned and chopped

salt and pepper

sprigs of fresh basil to garnish

Preparation time: 45 minutes
Cooking time: 30 minutes

Each serving provides ⓥ

kcal 245, protein 14 g, fat 16 g (of which saturated fat 7 g), carbohydrate 11 g (of which sugars 10 g), fibre 5 g

✓✓✓	A, C, E
✓✓	B₆, B₁₂, folate, niacin, calcium
✓	B₁, potassium

1 Dice the 2 outer (end) slices of aubergine, with the peel, and set aside to add to the filling. Use a third (2 tsp) of the olive oil to brush the remaining 8 aubergine slices sparingly on both sides. Heat a ridged griddle or frying pan and brown the aubergine slices for about 2 minutes on each side or until they are tender but not soft. Set aside on a board.

2 Add the remaining oil to the pan and cook the onion, half of the garlic, the red and green peppers, courgette and reserved diced aubergine for about 5 minutes or until softened. Add the parsley and half of the diced tomatoes, and continue to cook for a further 5–6 minutes.

3 Season the vegetable mixture, add the sugar and pour in the passata. Bring to the boil, then cover and cook over a low heat for about 10 minutes or until the mixture is richly flavoured and thickened.

4 In a bowl, combine the remaining garlic and diced tomatoes with the chopped basil, mozzarella and olives. Set this topping mixture aside. Preheat the oven to 180°C (350°F, gas mark 4).

5 Lightly season the aubergine slices. Place a generous portion of the braised vegetable filling at the wider end of one slice and roll up to enclose the filling. Repeat with the remaining aubergine slices and filling, placing the rolls side by side in an ovenproof dish.

6 Spoon the tomato and mozzarella mixture evenly over the top. Bake for about 30 minutes or until the cheese topping has melted. Garnish with basil sprigs and serve hot or warm.

Some more ideas

• Instead of the courgette in the vegetable mixture, use 1 bulb of fennel, sliced lengthways and separated into strips.

• For a quick dish, layer the aubergine slices and braised vegetables in an ovenproof dish, ending with a layer of aubergine on top. Sprinkle the mozzarella mixture over and bake as above.

Plus points

• Not only is mozzarella delicious with tomatoes and basil in this dish, but it also keeps the fat content modest as it contains less fat than other cheeses. Unlike some lower-fat cheeses, mozzarella is still rich in calcium, which is essential for healthy bones and teeth, muscle contraction, nerve function and proper clotting of the blood.

Veggie burgers

A few simple ingredients make really tasty meat-free burgers. If you want to barbecue them, the best method is to cook the burgers in advance and just heat them up over the coals, as this prevents them from sticking to the grilling rack. A crisp side salad is all that is needed with the burgers in their sesame-topped buns.

Serves 4

2½ tbsp extra virgin olive oil

1 large onion, finely chopped

1 garlic clove, finely chopped

300 g (10½ oz) carrots, coarsely grated

300 g (10½ oz) courgettes, coarsely grated

1½ tsp ground cumin

1½ tsp ground coriander

3 tbsp wholenut peanut butter

2 tbsp chopped fresh coriander

100 g (3½ oz) fresh wholemeal breadcrumbs

1 egg, beaten

salt and pepper

To serve

2 tomatoes, seeded and chopped

2 tbsp tomato ketchup, chutney or relish

4 sesame burger buns

2 tbsp mayonnaise (optional)

4 iceberg lettuce leaves, shredded

1 shallot, thinly sliced

Preparation time: 40 minutes
Cooking time: 10 minutes

Each serving provides   Ⓥ

kcal 480, **protein** 16 g, **fat** 20 g (of which saturated fat 4 g), **carbohydrate** 61 g (of which sugars 17 g), **fibre** 6 g

✓✓✓	A, B₁, C, folate
✓✓	B₆, E, niacin
✓	B₁₂, calcium, copper, iron, potassium, zinc

1 Heat 2 tbsp of the oil in a large non-stick frying pan. Add the onion and garlic, and cook over a moderate heat for 5 minutes, stirring frequently, until the onion is soft and beginning to brown. Add the carrots and courgettes, and fry for a further 10 minutes, stirring, until the vegetables have softened.

2 Stir in the ground cumin and coriander, the peanut butter, fresh coriander and seasoning to taste, and mix well. Remove the pan from the heat and set aside to cool slightly.

3 Mix in the breadcrumbs and egg until thoroughly combined. The mixture should bind together well. Shape the mixture into 4 thick burgers about 10 cm (4 in) in diameter.

4 Wipe out the pan with kitchen paper, then add and heat the remaining ½ tbsp of oil. Fry the burgers over a low to moderate heat for about 5 minutes on each side, or until they are firm and golden.

5 To serve, stir the tomatoes and ketchup together with seasoning to taste. Split the burger buns in half horizontally and toast the cut sides. Spread 1 tsp mayonnaise, if using, on each bun, then add some lettuce and a burger to each. Spread with the tomato mixture and top with the shallot slices. Replace the tops of the buns and serve.

Plus points

● Peanut butter contributes protein to these burgers, as does the wheat from the wholemeal breadcrumbs. Peanut butter is high in fat, but this is largely in a healthy monounsaturated form.

● Both onions and garlic contain allicin, a phytochemical that has anti-fungal and antibiotic properties.

Some more ideas

● For beef and veggie burgers, add 450 g (1 lb) lean minced beef to the cooled vegetable mixture with the breadcrumbs and egg. Omit the peanut butter. Add 1 tbsp chilli powder instead of the ground cumin and coriander, if preferred. Shape the mixture into 8 burgers. Grill the burgers for 10 minutes, turning once.

● These veggie burgers freeze well once cooked. Allow them to cool, then wrap them individually in cling film and place in a freezer bag to freeze. To serve, remove the required number, unwrap and reheat from frozen under a preheated moderate grill for about 15 minutes, turning occasionally, or for about 20 minutes in the oven at 200ºC (400ºF, gas mark 6), until thoroughly heated.

Broccoli and red pepper quiche

This vegetable-packed quiche is cooked in a large, deeper-than-average tin and the pastry is rolled out thinly to give a generous amount of filling and small proportion of pastry in each slice. Serve warm, rather than piping hot or chilled, with a lightly dressed, crisp salad.

Serves 8

15 g (½ oz) butter

1 tbsp extra virgin olive oil

225 g (8 oz) onions, thinly sliced

1 red pepper, seeded and finely chopped

85 g (3 oz) broccoli, cut into small florets

3 large eggs, beaten

225 ml (7½ fl oz) semi-skimmed milk

3 tbsp finely chopped parsley or fresh chives

125 g (4½ oz) shiitake mushrooms or small closed-cup mushrooms, sliced

115 g (4 oz) frozen sweetcorn, thawed and drained

salt and pepper

Pastry

125 g (4½ oz) plain flour

125 g (4½ oz) plain wholemeal flour

pinch of cayenne pepper (optional)

125 g (4½ oz) butter, chilled and diced

Preparation time: 1¼ hours, plus at least 30 minutes chilling

Cooking time: 40–45 minutes

Each serving provides Ⓥ

kcal 330, **protein** 9 g, **fat** 20 g (of which saturated fat 11 g), **carbohydrate** 32 g (of which sugars 5 g), **fibre** 3 g

✓✓✓	C
✓✓	A, B₁₂, E, folate
✓	B₁, niacin, calcium, iron, selenium

1 First make the pastry. Sift both types of flour and the cayenne pepper, if using, into a large bowl, adding the bran left in the sieve. Rub in the butter until the mixture resembles fine crumbs. Sprinkle with 2 tbsp of ice-cold water and mix to form a dough, adding an extra 1 tbsp water, if necessary.

2 Gather the dough into a ball, then roll it out on a lightly floured surface into a 28 cm (11 in) circle, about 3 mm (⅛ in) thick. Use the pastry to line a loose-bottomed 23 cm (9 in) fluted flan tin, about 3 cm (1¼ in) deep. Prick the pastry case all over with a fork, then cover and chill for at least 30 minutes.

3 Place a baking sheet in the oven and preheat it to 200°C (400°F, gas mark 6). Melt the butter with the olive oil in a frying pan or large saucepan. Add the onions and stir well, then cover and cook over a very low heat for 30 minutes or until very tender.

4 Meanwhile, blanch the red pepper in a saucepan of boiling water for 1 minute. Remove with a slotted spoon, place the pepper in a colander and refresh under cold water, then drain well. Add the broccoli to the same water and blanch for 30 seconds, then remove, refresh and drain well.

5 Line the chilled pastry case with a piece of greaseproof paper and cover with baking beans or rice. Place on the hot baking sheet and bake for 20 minutes. Remove the paper and beans, and continue baking the pastry case for 5 minutes. Brush the bottom of the pastry case with a little of the beaten egg and bake for a further 2 minutes. Remove from the oven, leaving the baking sheet inside. Reduce the oven to 190°C (375°F, gas mark 5).

6 Beat the milk with the eggs. Add the herbs and seasoning to taste. Spread the onions in the pastry case, then add the red pepper, broccoli, mushrooms and sweetcorn. Pour the egg mixture over the vegetables.

7 Place the quiche in the oven, on the hot baking sheet, and bake for 40–45 minutes or until the filling is set. Leave to cool for at least 10 minutes before serving.

Plus points

● Eggs have received a 'bad press' in recent years because of their cholesterol content, but they are an excellent source of many nutrients, including protein, iron and vitamins A, B group and E. They are also low in fat.

Some more ideas

• For a crisp Mediterranean-style pastry, low in saturated fat, replace the butter with 125 ml (4½ fl oz) olive oil. Use 2–4 tbsp lukewarm water rather than ice-cold. Gather the pastry together into a soft ball, then press it over the bottom and up the side of the flan tin, trimming off any excess pastry. This delicate pastry must be handled with care. Cover and chill for at least 30 minutes. Do not blind bake: add the filling to the uncooked pastry case and bake at 180ºC (350ºF, gas mark 4) for 55–60 minutes. Leave the quiche to set and cool before serving. Cut it with a serrated knife.

• Other suitable vegetables to include are finely chopped seeded tomatoes, shelled peas and sliced courgettes. For an aniseed-like flavour, soften a thinly sliced bulb of fennel with the onions. Chopped, well-drained cooked spinach can also be added, spread out in a thin layer over the onions.

Leek and spring green filo pie

A combination of spring vegetables, lively herbs and zesty lemon makes a refreshing filling for a crisp filo crust. This pie is easy to make and so delicious, it is destined to become a firm family favourite. For a hearty meal, serve it with baby carrots and new potatoes boiled in their skins.

Serves 4

finely grated zest of 1 lemon
2 tbsp extra virgin olive oil
225 g (8 oz) leeks, thinly sliced
115 g (4 oz) spring greens, thinly sliced
170 g (6 oz) frozen petits pois
2 tbsp chopped fresh tarragon
1 tbsp chopped fresh mint
2 large eggs
4 tbsp plain low-fat yogurt
85 g (3 oz) Gruyère cheese, diced
115 g (4 oz) filo pastry
salt and pepper

Preparation time: 20 minutes
Cooking time: 20–25 minutes

Each serving provides Ⓥ

kcal 300, **protein** 18 g, **fat** 18 g (of which saturated fat 6 g), **carbohydrate** 15 g (of which sugars 6 g), **fibre** 5 g

✓✓✓	B₁₂, C, folate, calcium
✓✓	A, B₁, B₂, B₆, E, niacin, iron
✓	zinc

1 Mix the lemon zest with the oil and set aside to infuse for about 5 minutes. Heat half the lemon-infused oil in a large saucepan. Add the leeks, spring greens, petits pois, tarragon and mint. Mix well to coat the vegetables with the oil, then cover and cook over a low heat for about 5 minutes, stirring occasionally, until the greens are lightly cooked and have wilted.

2 Season the vegetables to taste, then transfer them to a 20 cm (8 in) pie dish or flan dish. Preheat the oven to 220°C (425°F, gas mark 7).

3 Beat the eggs with the yogurt. Add a little seasoning and the Gruyère cheese, then pour the mixture evenly over the vegetables and mix lightly.

4 Brush a sheet of filo pastry very sparingly with a little of the remaining lemon-infused oil and lay it over the vegetables, tucking the edges neatly inside the rim of the dish. Brush the remaining sheets of filo with oil and place them on top of the pie, oiled side up, pinching and pleating them into folds to cover the top fairly evenly.

5 Lay a piece of foil loosely over the top of the pie, and bake for about 10 minutes. Remove the foil and bake for a further 10–15 minutes or until the pastry is crisp and golden brown. Serve immediately.

Some more ideas

● Replace the spring greens and petit pois with mushrooms and spinach. Slice 125 g (4½ oz) button mushrooms and cook with the leeks and herbs, adding 2 garlic cloves, crushed, and 1 bunch of spring onions, sliced. Place in the bottom of the pie dish. Wash 225 g (8 oz) spinach and place in a saucepan, then cover and cook for about 2 minutes or until the leaves are wilted and tender (the water remaining on the leaves will provide sufficient moisture). Drain well, pressing out excess liquid, then coarsely chop the spinach and place on top of the mushrooms. Sprinkle evenly with 100 g (3½ oz) crumbled feta cheese and pour over the egg and yogurt mixture (omit the Gruyère). Top with the filo and bake.

● Curly kale and chickpeas are another good combination. Use 115 g (4 oz) kale, shredded, and 1 can chickpeas, about 400 g, drained, instead of the spring greens and petit pois.

Plus points

● Filo pastry can be cooked with just a little fat to give light and crisp results. It is an ideal alternative to rich pastries.

● Like other dark green, leafy vegetables, spring greens are an excellent source of antioxidant carotenoids which help to prevent degenerative diseases.

Potato-filled Sardinian ravioli

Mashed potato enriched with cottage cheese and Parmesan and enlivened with garlic and herbs makes a marvellous filling for the pasta parcels called ravioli. A small amount of extra virgin olive oil is added at the end, so none of its flavour is lost and the dish tastes richer than it really is.

Serves 6

500 g (1 lb 2 oz) potatoes, peeled, boiled and mashed

3 tbsp cottage cheese, sieved

5 spring onions, thinly sliced

2 tbsp chopped parsley

4 tsp coarsely chopped fresh thyme

4 tbsp freshly grated Parmesan cheese

4 garlic cloves, chopped

1 egg, beaten

450 g (1 lb) ripe tomatoes, diced, or 1 can chopped tomatoes, about 400 g, drained

1 tbsp extra virgin olive oil

Pasta dough

450 g (1 lb) strong plain flour

4 eggs, beaten

1 tbsp extra virgin olive oil

salt and pepper

Preparation time: about 1½ hours, plus 1 hour resting

Cooking time: 5–10 minutes

Each serving provides (V)

kcal 480, **protein** 21 g, **fat** 13 g (of which saturated fat 4 g), **carbohydrate** 73 g (of which sugars 4 g), **fibre** 4 g

✓✓✓	B_{12}
✓✓	B_1, C, E, folate, niacin, calcium, iron, selenium
✓	A, B_2, copper, potassium, zinc

1 First make the pasta dough. Place the flour in a bowl, add a pinch of salt and make a well in the centre. Add the eggs and oil. Gradually work in the flour, using a fork at first, then your hands, and adding 1–2 tbsp water, if necessary, to make a firm dough. Knead for 5–10 minutes or until smooth. Place in a polythene bag and leave at room temperature to rest for 1 hour.

2 Mix the mashed potatoes with the cottage cheese, spring onions, parsley, and half of the thyme, Parmesan cheese and garlic. Add seasoning to taste, then mix in the egg.

3 Cut the pasta into quarters. Replace 3 portions in the bag while you roll out the first piece very thinly to make an oblong about 20 x 50 cm (8 x 20 in). Keep this covered while you roll out a second portion to the same size.

4 Dot teaspoonfuls of the filling in mounds over one sheet of pasta, placing them about 5 cm (2 in) apart. You should have 21 mounds, in 7 rows of 3. Brush between the filling with water and top with the second sheet of pasta. Press the dough together between the mounds of filling, then cut along the sealed area using a fluted pastry wheel or sharp knife. Separate the ravioli and place on a lightly floured plate. Repeat with the remaining pasta and filling.

5 If the ravioli are to be left for any length of time, dust them with flour and cover loosely with cling film, then place in the refrigerator. Cook within 24 hours or freeze.

6 Gently warm the tomatoes with seasoning to taste in a saucepan over a low heat. Cook the ravioli in a large saucepan of boiling water for about 3 minutes or until they are just tender. Drain well.

7 Arrange the ravioli in warmed serving dishes and top with the warmed tomatoes, and the remaining garlic, thyme and Parmesan cheese. Sprinkle with the olive oil and serve.

Plus points

• Mixing a bland cheese such as cottage cheese with Parmesan is a good way to boost the flavour without increasing the fat too much.

• The value of potatoes as a nutritious and satisfying food was recognised during the Second World War by the Ministry of Food, which took steps to ensure that potatoes were readily available and that they were never rationed.

Some more ideas

● Make folded 'ravioli', using fresh lasagne sheets. Cook 250 g (9 oz) lasagne, a few sheets at a time, in rapidly boiling water for 3 minutes or following the packet instructions. Refresh in cold water and drain well. Place a little filling on one half of a sheet of lasagne and fold it over.

Lay the 'ravioli' in a greased ovenproof dish. Repeat with the remaining lasagne and filling. Heat the tomatoes with the remaining garlic and thyme and the olive oil. Pour over the pasta and sprinkle evenly with the remaining Parmesan. Bake at 200ºC (400ºF, gas mark 6) for about 10 minutes or until piping hot.

● The ravioli can be cooked in advance, then cooled and chilled until required. Add the tomatoes, oil and remaining garlic, thyme and Parmesan shortly before serving, and reheat in the oven preheated to 200ºC (400ºF, gas mark 6) for about 5 minutes. The tomato and Parmesan topping should be lightly browned.

Vegetables on the Side

New ideas to enhance healthy menus

TEMPTING VEGETABLE ACCOMPANIMENTS will encourage everyone to eat more vegetables. A simple dressing or topping often does the trick – sprinkle crisp crumbs with herbs over plain vegetables. A little spice, some herbs or olive oil makes a delicious alternative to butter, especially in creamy vegetable purées. Cook different vegetables together – roast mixed root vegetables, or braise baby leeks, parsnips, carrots and onions in a little stock. Why not introduce exotic flavours? Finely shredded nori, a type of Japanese seaweed, tastes terrific with new potatoes.

Cauliflower with crispy crumbs

The crispy golden topping in this simple side dish is usually made by frying the breadcrumbs in a generous quantity of butter. This version uses a modest portion of olive oil and fresh herbs to flavour a topping that tastes good with all steamed or boiled vegetables, and contrasts particularly well with steamed cauliflower.

Serves 4

1 cauliflower, trimmed and broken into florets

Crispy crumb topping

2 tbsp extra virgin olive oil

100 g (3½ oz) fresh breadcrumbs

1 tbsp chopped fresh thyme

1 tbsp chopped fresh tarragon

2 tbsp chopped parsley

salt and pepper

sprigs of fresh herbs to garnish (optional)

Preparation time: 10 minutes

Cooking time: 15 minutes

1 Prepare a saucepan of boiling water with a steamer on top. Steam the cauliflower for about 15 minutes or until tender but not soft.

2 Meanwhile, heat the oil in a non-stick frying pan or saucepan. Add the breadcrumbs and stir well to coat the crumbs as evenly as possible with oil. Cook over a moderate heat, stirring often, for about 10 minutes or until the crumbs are well browned and crisp. As the crumbs cook, the oil will seep out of those that absorbed it initially, allowing the rest to become evenly crisp.

3 Transfer the cauliflower to a warm serving dish. Season the crumbs to taste and mix in the thyme, tarragon and parsley. Sprinkle the crumb mixture over the cauliflower. Garnish with sprigs of herbs, if using, and serve.

Some more ideas

● The crumb topping also goes well with lightly cooked Brussels sprouts (boiled or steamed). Use chopped fresh sage or marjoram instead of the tarragon and add the grated zest of 1 lemon to the crumb mixture. Serve lemon wedges with the sprouts so that the juice can be squeezed over.

● The crisp crumbs are delicious with hot beetroot. Use fresh sage instead of the tarragon and add the grated zest of 1 orange to the crumb mixture. To serve, thickly slice the freshly boiled beetroot, arrange overlapping on a serving platter, and sprinkle with the crumb mixture. Garnish with orange slices. This goes well with roast or grilled pork, gammon or sausages.

● Celeriac is another vegetable that is enhanced by a crisp crumb topping. Cut the celeriac into small cubes, fingers or slices before cooking. For a delicate topping, Instead of the herbs listed in the main recipe use 3 tbsp finely chopped fresh dill. Celeriac garnished in this way is super with grilled, poached or baked white fish.

Plus points

● Cauliflower is a member of the brassica family of cruciferous vegetables. It contains sulphurous compounds thought to help protect against cancer. It also provides vitamin C and fibre.

● The positive features of bread have often been overlooked, as it has quite unfairly gained a reputation for being fattening: it is what you put on the bread, not the bread itself, that can be fattening. Even white bread provides good amounts of dietary fibre, and by law it is fortified with vitamins and minerals, including B_1 and calcium.

Each serving provides Ⓥ

kcal 180, **protein** 7 g, **fat** 7 g (of which saturated fat 1 g), **carbohydrate** 23 g (of which sugars 4 g), **fibre** 3 g

✓✓✓	C
✓✓	folate
✓	B_1, B_6, niacin

vegetables on the side

Sweet potato and celeriac purée

Mashes and purées are perennial favourites and an excellent way of boosting your daily intake of vegetables. They are so easy to eat that all the family will enjoy them in generous quantities. This sweet potato and celeriac purée is deliciously flavoured with apple and spices, and there are 2 more suggestions to tempt you.

Serves 4

500 g (1 lb 2 oz) sweet potato

400 g (14 oz) celeriac

juice of 1 lemon

2 tbsp extra virgin olive oil

2 garlic cloves, finely chopped

1 tbsp coarsely grated fresh root ginger

½–1 tsp ground cumin

1 Golden Delicious apple, peeled, cored and finely chopped

1 tbsp coriander seeds, roughly crushed

Preparation time: 15 minutes
Cooking time: 15–20 minutes

1 Cut the sweet potato and celeriac into similar-sized chunks and place in a large saucepan. Add half the lemon juice, then pour in boiling water to cover the vegetables and bring back to the boil. Reduce the heat and simmer gently for 15–20 minutes or until the vegetables are tender.

2 Meanwhile, heat the oil in a small saucepan. Add the garlic, ginger and cumin, and cook for 30 seconds. Stir in the apple and remaining lemon juice and cook for 5 minutes or until the apple begins to soften.

3 Toast the crushed coriander seeds in a small dry pan, stirring occasionally, until they are fragrant.

4 Drain the vegetables well, then mash them. Stir in the apple mixture and sprinkle with the toasted coriander seeds. Serve piping hot.

Some more ideas

• For a creamy root vegetable purée, use 3 carrots, 3 parsnips and 1 small swede, about 900 g (2 lb) in total. Cut into similar-sized chunks and place in a large saucepan. Pour in boiling water to cover and bring back to the boil. Reduce the heat and simmer for 20–25 minutes or until the vegetables are tender. Drain well. Add 5 tbsp Greek-style yogurt to the vegetables and mash until smooth. (Alternatively, purée in a food processor.) Stir in 4 spring onions, finely chopped, and seasoning to taste. Transfer to a serving dish and sprinkle with toasted flaked almonds.

• For a chilli-spiced split pea purée, rinse 225 g (8 oz) yellow split peas in cold water, drain and place in a saucepan. Add 2 whole garlic cloves (if liked) and pour in boiling water to cover the peas generously. Bring to the boil, then reduce the heat and simmer for about 1 hour or until tender. Drain well. Mash the peas with about 5 tbsp semi-skimmed milk and 30 g (1 oz) butter using a vegetable masher, or purée in a food processor. Stir in 2 small fresh red chillies, seeded and finely chopped; 4 tbsp chopped fresh coriander or parsley; 8 sprigs of fresh basil, tough stalks discarded, then shredded; and seasoning to taste.

Each serving provides ⓥ

kcal 140, **protein** 3 g, **fat** 1.5 g (of which saturated fat 0.2 g), **carbohydrate** 32 g (of which sugars 12 g), **fibre** 7 g

✓✓✓	A, C, E
✓✓	folate
✓	B₁, B₆, potassium

Plus points

• Sweet potatoes are an excellent source of beta-carotene, an antioxidant that helps to protect against free radical damage, which can age us and increase the risk of heart disease and cancer. Sweet potatoes also provide good amounts of vitamin C and potassium, and contain more vitamin E than any other vegetable.

New potatoes with nori

From the same botanical family known as laver in Wales, slouk in Scotland and sloke in Ireland, nori is a type of Japanese seaweed, sold dried in thin, dark-green sheets. The flavour is distinctive and savoury. Nori is usually combined with rice in Japanese cooking, but it is also good with vegetables, particularly potatoes.

Serves 4

500 g (1 lb 2 oz) new potatoes
30 g (1 oz) butter
grated zest and juice of ½ small lemon
1 sheet toasted sushi nori, about 20 x 18 cm
   (8 x 7 in)
2 tbsp snipped fresh chives
salt and pepper

Preparation time: 5 minutes
Cooking time: 15 minutes

1 Put the new potatoes in a saucepan, cover with boiling water and bring back to the boil. Cook for 12 minutes or until they are just tender.

2 Reserve 3 tbsp cooking water from the potatoes, then drain them and return them to the saucepan with the reserved water. Add the butter and lemon zest and juice. Turn the potatoes to coat them with the liquid.

3 Use scissors to snip the sushi nori into fine strips. Sprinkle the nori over the potatoes and cover the pan. Cook over a low heat for 1–2 minutes or until the nori has softened. Add seasoning to taste. Sprinkle with the chives and serve immediately.

Some more ideas

• Sushi nori is rather like parchment paper in texture. Toasted or roasted sushi nori has been toasted briefly and seasoned. It is shiny and almost black in colour – untoasted nori is slightly paler (more green) in colour. To toast nori, pass the sheet over the flame of a gas hob, once on each side of the sheet, or lay the sheet on a rack in a grill pan and place under a preheated grill for a few seconds. The sheet will darken and give off its aroma very quickly – take care not to overcook the nori or it will burn.

• Green beans go well with lemon and potatoes, and can be added to the dish or used to replace the nori. Snip 200 g (7 oz) French beans into short pieces and add them to the potatoes about halfway through the cooking: 4–5 minutes is sufficient time for cooking the beans. Drain and toss with the butter and lemon zest and juice.

• Look out for yard-long or asparagus beans, which, as their name suggests, grow to an amazing length. Their flavour is similar to that of runner beans and they are good with the potatoes and nori. Prepare them as for green beans (above).

Plus points

• Nori is rich in vitamin A and minerals, including potassium, which helps to counteract the effects of sodium and keep blood pressure down. Nori also contains iron, zinc, copper and iodine.

• New potatoes and lemon juice contribute vitamin C, which promotes absorption of iron from the nori.

Each serving provides Ⓥ

kcal 160, **protein** 6 g, **fat** 7 g (of which saturated fat 4 g), **carbohydrate** 20 g (of which sugars 2 g), **fibre** 7 g

✓✓✓	B$_{12}$
✓✓	A, B$_6$, C, E
✓	B$_1$, B$_2$, copper, iron, potassium, zinc

Braised baby vegetables

Slowly braising whole baby vegetables preserves and enriches their flavours, and reducing the cooking juices in the final stages of cooking creates a delicious dressing that makes an attractive glaze. Using the cooking liquid in this way retains the water-soluble vitamins. These vegetables are perfect with roast poultry, game or meat.

Serves 4

4 baby leeks, about 200 g (7 oz) in total
250 g (9 oz) baby parsnips
30 g (1 oz) butter
250 g (9 oz) baby carrots
8 pickling onions or shallots
150 ml (5 fl oz) vegetable stock, preferably
    home-made (see page 28)
1 tsp sugar
1 bay leaf
pepper

Preparation time: 15 minutes
Cooking time: 25–30 minutes

1 Trim the leeks and split them lengthways without cutting them completely in half. Open out and wash under running water to remove any dirt. Cut the parsnips in half lengthways.

2 Melt the butter in a large saucepan or flameproof casserole. Add all the vegetables. Stir in the stock, sugar, bay leaf and pepper to taste. Bring to the boil, then cover and reduce the heat to the lowest setting.

3 Cook for 20–25 minutes or until the vegetables are barely tender. Remove the lid and boil the liquid for 2–3 minutes or until bubbling and reduced to a thick syrup-like glaze. Turn the vegetables in the glaze, discard the bay leaf and serve immediately.

Some more ideas

● Use 4 whole baby cauliflowers instead of the carrots and parsnips. Add the baby cauliflowers for the last 8 minutes of cooking.
● When baby vegetables are not available, use ordinary vegetables and cut them into chunks or large pieces.
● Add the grated zest and juice of 1 orange with the stock.
● Stir in snipped fresh chives or chopped parsley just before serving the vegetables.

Plus points

● Leeks and parsnips both provide useful amounts of folate, which is important for proper blood cell formation and development of the nervous system in an unborn baby.
● Carrots are a valuable source of vitamin A in the form of beta-carotene, which gives them their vibrant orange colour. Unlike most vegetables, which are most nutritious when eaten raw, carrots have more nutritional value when cooked. Because raw carrots have tough cell walls, the body can convert only about 25% of the beta-carotene present into vitamin A. Cooking breaks down the cell membrane in the carrots, making it easier for the body to absorb and convert the beta-carotene.

Each serving provides Ⓥ

kcal 155, **protein** 3 g, **fat** 7 g (of which saturated fat 4 g), **carbohydrate** 19 g (of which sugars 13 g), **fibre** 6 g

✓✓✓	A
✓✓	B$_1$, C, E, folate
✓	B$_6$

vegetables on the side

Roast root vegetables with herbs

Use this recipe as a basic guide for roasting single vegetables, such as potatoes or parsnips, as well as for a superb dish of mixed roots. Serve them in generous quantities with roast poultry or meat, but also remember that they are delicious with vegetarian main dishes and with lightly baked fish.

Serves 4

1 kg (2¼ lb) root vegetables, such as
   potatoes, sweet potatoes, carrots, parsnips,
   swede and kohlrabi
225 g (8 oz) shallots or pickling onions
2 tbsp extra virgin olive oil
1 tsp coarse sea salt
1 tsp cracked black peppercorns
few sprigs of fresh thyme
few sprigs of fresh rosemary
sprigs of fresh thyme or rosemary to garnish
   (optional)

Preparation time: 15–20 minutes
Cooking time: 30–35 minutes

Each serving provides (V)
kcal 200, **protein** 4 g, **fat** 7 g (of which
saturated fat 1 g), **carbohydrate** 33 g (of
which sugars 14 g), **fibre** 7 g

✓✓✓	A, C
✓✓	B₁, B₆, E, folate
✓	niacin, potassium

1 Preheat the oven to 220°C (425°F, gas mark 7). Scrub or peel the vegetables, according to type and your taste. Halve or quarter large potatoes. Cut large carrots or parsnips in half lengthways, then cut the pieces across in half again. Cut swede or kohlrabi into large chunks (about the same size as the potatoes). Leave shallots or onions whole.

2 Place the vegetables in a saucepan and pour in enough boiling water to cover them. Bring back to the boil, then reduce the heat and simmer for 5–7 minutes or until the vegetables are lightly cooked, but not yet tender.

3 Drain the vegetables and place them in a roasting tin. Brush with the oil and sprinkle with the salt and peppercorns. Add the herb sprigs to the tin and place in the oven.

4 Roast for 30–35 minutes or until the vegetables are golden brown, crisp and tender. Turn the vegetables over halfway through the cooking. Serve hot, garnished with sprigs of thyme or rosemary, if liked.

Some more ideas

● The vegetables can be roasted at the same time as a joint of meat or poultry. Allow 45 minutes at 200°C (400°F, gas mark 6), or longer at a lower temperature, if necessary.
● Baby new vegetables can also be roasted. For example, try new potatoes, carrots, beetroot and turnips. As well as root vegetables, patty pan squash and asparagus are delicious roasted. Sprinkle with herbs and a little balsamic vinegar or lemon juice.
● Quartered acorn squash is good roasted with mixed root vegetables.

Plus points

● Combining different root vegetables instead of serving roast potatoes alone provides a good mix of flavours and nutrients: as well as vitamin C from the potatoes and beta-carotene from the carrots, swedes are part of the brassica family, which offer cancer-fighting phytochemicals.
● All these vegetables provide plenty of flavour and satisfying bulk, so portions of meat can be modest. They also contribute dietary fibre.

vegetables on the side

Baked pumpkin with red onion and sage

Pumpkin is a versatile and easy-to-cook accompaniment for all sorts of main dishes, as are the other squashes that can be used in this recipe. Club-shaped butternut squash is available for most of the year, and in autumn there are small acorn squash, kabocha squash and Prince Regent squash with its eggshell blue skin.

Serves 4

1 small pumpkin, about 1.6 kg (3½ lb),
   peeled, seeded and cubed, or 900 g (2 lb)
   prepared pumpkin flesh, cubed
2 red onions, cut into wedges
4 garlic cloves, thinly sliced
3 tbsp chopped fresh sage
2 tbsp extra virgin olive oil
salt and pepper

Preparation time: 20–25 minutes
Cooking time: 35 minutes

1 Preheat the oven to 220°C (425°F, gas mark 7). Lay a large sheet of foil on a baking tray. Pile the pumpkin and onions in the middle of the foil. Alternatively, prepare 4 sheets of foil and cook the pumpkin in individual parcels.

2 Scatter the garlic and sage over the pumpkin, then drizzle the oil over and add seasoning to taste. Fold up the foil to enclose the pumpkin, then fold the edges together to seal the vegetables inside a neat parcel.

3 Bake the pumpkin parcel or parcels for 30 minutes, then open the foil and bake for a further 5 minutes or until the pumpkin is tender and beginning to brown. Serve hot.

Some more ideas

• To make a substantial snack or light meal, toss 200 g (7 oz) feta cheese, diced, with the cooked pumpkin. Cut a part-baked ciabatta loaf in half, then slice each half in two horizontally. Lightly toast the cut sides of the bread, then pile the pumpkin mixture on top and grill for about 5 minutes or until golden brown. Serve hot with a mixed salad.

• Try fresh thyme, oregano or rosemary with the pumpkin instead of sage. They all taste good with the slightly sweet vegetable.

Plus points

• Until quite recently, pumpkin only appeared in the shops for a short period around Halloween and then was used mainly for making lanterns. Now pumpkin is available for most of the autumn and winter. This delicious vegetable is a good source of fibre and a useful source of vitamin B_1.

• Onions and garlic are not just valuable assets in the kitchen, they have been used throughout history as a cure-all. Recent research suggests that they can help to lower blood cholesterol and so reduce the risk of heart disease.

Each serving provides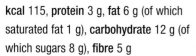

kcal 115, **protein** 3 g, **fat** 6 g (of which saturated fat 1 g), **carbohydrate** 12 g (of which sugars 8 g), **fibre** 5 g

✓✓✓	A, C, E
✓✓	B_1
✓	folate, calcium

vegetables on the side

148

Basil-scented sautéed vegetables

A large non-stick frying pan is ideal for sautéeing, the Western equivalent of stir-frying, based on quick cooking over high heat. This is a terrific method for preserving the colour of vegetables while bringing out their flavour to the full. Serve the vegetables with fish, poultry or meat, or toss them with freshly cooked noodles.

Serves 4

500 g (1 lb 2 oz) broccoli
1 tbsp extra virgin olive oil
3–4 large garlic cloves, thinly sliced (optional)
1 large or 2 small red peppers, seeded and
    cut into chunks
1 turnip, about 150 g (5½ oz), cut into
    bite-sized chunks
pinch of sugar
8 sprigs of fresh basil, stalks discarded, then
    finely shredded
salt

Preparation time: 10 minutes
Cooking time: 7–8 minutes

1 Cut the broccoli into small florets; trim and thinly slice the stalks. Heat the olive oil in a large non-stick frying pan or wok. Add the garlic, if using, the red pepper, turnip and slices of broccoli stalk. Sprinkle in the sugar and salt to taste. Cook for 2–3 minutes, turning frequently.

2 Add the broccoli florets and stir. Pour in 6 tbsp of water to provide a thin covering on the bottom of the pan. Cover and cook over a fairly high heat for 3–4 minutes. The broccoli should be just tender and bright green.

3 Stir in the basil, replace the lid and leave on the heat for a few more seconds. Serve immediately.

Some more ideas

- For a Far-Eastern flavour, substitute 8 canned water chestnuts, drained and quartered or halved, for the turnips, and add 1 tsp chopped fresh root ginger and ½ fresh green or red chilli, seeded and finely chopped, with the broccoli florets. Increase the quantity of sugar to 1–2 tsp. At the end of cooking, add 1 tbsp chopped fresh coriander with the basil.

- Sugarsnap peas or mange-tout can be used instead of the broccoli. They will cook in 1–2 minutes and there is no need to add the water. Serve with lemon or lime wedges so that the juice can be squeezed over the vegetables.

- As well as replacing the broccoli with sugarsnap peas, use yellow peppers in place of red. Omit the garlic. Substitute tiny parboiled new potatoes, halved, for the turnip and sprinkle generously with fresh tarragon leaves rather than basil. This combination of sautéed vegetables is delicious with fish, especially grilled mackerel or salmon.

Plus points

- This dish is loaded with ingredients that help to fight cancer and prevent heart disease. Broccoli, one of the brassicas, is a good source of the phytochemicals called glucosinolates. Red pepper is a rich source of the antioxidant beta-carotene which the body can convert into vitamin A.
- In addition to providing fibre, turnips contain the B vitamins niacin and B_6, and are a surprisingly useful source of vitamin C.

Each serving provides Ⓥ

kcal 90, **protein** 6 g, **fat** 4 g (of which saturated fat 1 g), **carbohydrate** 7 g (of which sugars 7 g), **fibre** 5 g

✓✓✓	A, C
✓✓	E, folate
✓	niacin, iron

Sesame greens and bean sprouts

With a little inspiration and the availability of international ingredients, even the most humble vegetables can be elevated to feature in unusual, well-flavoured side dishes. This succulent stir-fry is full of flavour and crunch. It is ideal as part of an Oriental menu or equally delicious with plain grilled fish, poultry or meat.

Serves 4

30 g (1 oz) sesame seeds
2 tbsp sunflower oil
1 onion, chopped
2 garlic cloves, chopped
1 small Savoy cabbage, about 300 g
    (10½ oz), finely shredded
½ head of Chinese leaves, finely shredded
170 g (6 oz) bean sprouts
4 tbsp oyster sauce
salt and pepper

Preparation time: 10 minutes
Cooking time: 4–6 minutes

1 Heat a small saucepan and dry-fry the sesame seeds, shaking the pan frequently, until they are just beginning to brown. Turn the seeds out into a small bowl and set aside.

2 Heat the oil in a wok or large frying pan. Add the onion and garlic, and stir-fry for 2–3 minutes or until softened slightly. Add the cabbage and Chinese leaves and stir-fry over a fairly high heat for 2–3 minutes or until the vegetables are just beginning to soften. Add the bean sprouts and continue cooking for a few seconds.

3 Make a space in the centre of the pan. Pour in the oyster sauce and 2 tbsp of water, and stir until hot, then toss the vegetables into the sauce. Taste and add pepper, with salt if necessary (this will depend on the saltiness of the oyster sauce). Serve immediately, sprinkled with the toasted sesame seeds.

Some more ideas

- Use 250 g (9 oz) red cabbage, finely shredded, instead of the Savoy cabbage, and add 3 cooked beetroot, chopped, with the bean sprouts. Red cabbage will require 2 minutes additional stir-frying, so add to the wok before the Chinese leaves. Use 1 tbsp clear honey with 2 tbsp soy sauce instead of the oyster sauce.
- Finely shredded Brussels sprouts are crisp and full flavoured when stir-fried. Use them instead of the Savoy cabbage – slice the sprouts thinly, then shake the slices to loosen the shreds. Or use shredded spring greens. Toasted flaked almonds can be sprinkled over the vegetables instead of the sesame seeds.

Plus points

- As well as contributing distinctive flavour, sesame seeds are a good source of calcium and therefore useful for anyone who dislikes or does not eat dairy products, the main source of this mineral in the Western diet. A combination of good supplies of calcium and plenty of physical activity are particularly important for young girls so as to avoid osteoporosis later in life.
- Bean sprouts, along with other sprouted seeds, are rich in B vitamins and vitamin C. They also provide iron and potassium.

Each serving provides

kcal 150, **protein** 5 g, **fat** 11 g (of which saturated fat 1 g), **carbohydrate** 9 g (of which sugars 5 g), **fibre** 4 g

✓✓✓	C, folate
✓✓	B$_{12}$
✓	B$_1$, calcium, iron, potassium

vegetables on the side

Indian-style okra with potatoes

This makes a wonderful accompaniment to a spicy main dish. It is also good as a vegetarian main course for 2, especially when served with Indian-style pulse or lentil dishes and warm naan bread. Also known as ladies' fingers or bhindi, *okra is used extensively in Indian, Caribbean and South American cooking.*

Serves 4

1 large onion, quartered

4 garlic cloves

5 cm (2 in) piece of fresh root ginger, peeled

2 tbsp sunflower oil

1 fresh red or green chilli, seeded and finely
    chopped

1 tsp black mustard seeds

2 tsp ground coriander

1 tsp ground cumin

1 tsp turmeric

450 ml (15 fl oz) hot vegetable stock,
    preferably home-made (see page 28)

1 can chopped tomatoes, about 400 g

200 g (7 oz) okra, trimmed and sliced

500 g (1 lb 2 oz) potatoes, peeled and cut
    into large chunks

1 red, green or yellow pepper, seeded and
    cut into chunks

4 tbsp raisins

3 tbsp chopped fresh coriander

salt and pepper

chopped fresh coriander to garnish

Preparation time: 15 minutes

Cooking time: 35–40 minutes

1 Put the onion, peeled garlic and ginger in a food processor or blender and purée. Alternatively, finely chop the ingredients and mix well together. Heat the oil in a saucepan. Add the onion purée and the chilli, and fry over a low heat for 6–7 minutes or until the mixture is beginning to turn golden brown in places.

2 Add the mustard seeds, ground coriander, cumin and turmeric, and stir to form a paste. Gradually pour in the stock and tomatoes with their juice, stirring well. Bring to the boil, then reduce the heat and cover the pan. Simmer over a low heat for 10 minutes or until the spices are cooked and their flavours blended.

3 Add the okra, potatoes, pepper, raisins and seasoning to taste. Stir well, then cover again and simmer over a low heat for 15–20 minutes or until the potatoes are tender.

4 Stir in the chopped coriander and serve at once, sprinkled with extra coriander to garnish.

Some more ideas

● To make a spicy coconut curry with cauliflower and chickpeas, add 55 g (2 oz) creamed coconut and a bay leaf with the stock. Use 700 g (1 lb 9 oz) cauliflower, cut into florets, instead of the potatoes, and 1 can chickpeas, about 420 g, drained, instead of the okra. Add the chickpeas at the end of step 3, when the cauliflower is cooked. Sprinkle in 3 spring onions, finely chopped, with the chickpeas. Sultanas can be used instead of raisins. Serve with poppadoms.

● If you are serving this as a vegetarian main dish, accompany it with plain or spiced basmati rice tossed with flaked almonds or chopped cashew nuts.

Plus points

● Fresh coriander is prescribed by herbalists as a tonic for the stomach and heart. Its seeds and leaves are recommended for urinary tract problems.

● In addition to the delicious spiciness it brings to the dish, ginger also aids digestion.

Each serving provides

kcal 285, **protein 7 g, fat 7 g (of which saturated fat 1 g), carbohydrate 52 g (of which sugars 29 g), fibre 6 g**

✓✓✓	C, E
✓✓	A, B₁, B₆, folate, potassium
✓	niacin, copper, iron

vegetables on the side

A glossary of nutritional terms

Antioxidants These are compounds that help to protect the body's cells against the damaging effects of free radicals. Vitamins C and E, beta-carotene (the plant form of vitamin A) and the mineral selenium, together with many of the phytochemicals found in fruit and vegetables, all act as antioxidants.

Calorie A unit used to measure the energy value of food and the intake and use of energy by the body. The scientific definition of 1 calorie is the amount of heat required to raise the temperature of 1 gram of water by 1 degree Centigrade. This is such a small amount that in this country we tend to use the term kilocalories (abbreviated to *kcal*), which is equivalent to 1000 calories. Energy values can also be measured in kilojoules (kJ): 1 kcal = 4.2 kJ.

A person's energy (calorie) requirement varies depending on his or her age, sex and level of activity. The estimated average daily energy requirements are:

Age (years)	Female (kcal)	Male (kcal)
1–3	1165	1230
4–6	1545	1715
7–10	1740	1970
11–14	1845	2220
15–18	2110	2755
19–49	1940	2550
50–59	1900	2550
60–64	1900	2380
65–74	1900	2330

Carbohydrates These energy-providing substances are present in varying amounts in different foods and are found in three main forms: sugars, starches and non-starch polysaccharides (NSP), usually called fibre.

There are two types of sugars: *intrinsic sugars*, which occur naturally in fruit (fructose) and sweet-tasting vegetables, and *extrinsic sugars*, which include lactose (from milk) and all the non-milk extrinsic sugars (NMEs) – sucrose (table sugar), honey, treacle, molasses and so on. The NMEs, or 'added' sugars, provide only calories, whereas foods containing intrinsic sugars also offer vitamins, minerals and fibre. Added sugars (*simple carbohydrates*) are digested and absorbed rapidly to provide energy very quickly. Starches and fibre (*complex carbohydrates*), on the other hand, break down more slowly to offer a longer-term energy source (see also Glycaemic Index). Starchy carbohydrates are found in bread, pasta, rice, wholegrain and breakfast cereals, and potatoes and other starchy vegetables such as parsnips, sweet potatoes and yams.

Healthy eating guidelines recommend that at least half of our daily energy (calories) should come from carbohydrates, and that most of this should be from complex carbohydrates. No more than 11% of our total calorie intake should come from 'added' sugars. For an average woman aged 19–49 years, this would mean a total carbohydrate intake of 259 g per day, of which 202 g should be from starch and intrinsic sugars and no more than 57 g from added sugars. For a man of the same age, total carbohydrates each day should be about 340 g (265 g from starch and intrinsic sugars and 75 g from added sugars).

See also Fibre and Glycogen.

Cholesterol There are two types of cholesterol – the soft waxy substance called blood cholesterol, which is an integral part of human cell membranes, and dietary cholesterol, which is contained in food. *Blood cholesterol* is important in the formation of some hormones and it aids digestion. High blood cholesterol levels are known to be an important risk factor for coronary heart disease, but most of the cholesterol in our blood is made by the liver – only about 25% comes from cholesterol in food. So while it would seem that the amount of cholesterol-rich foods in the diet would have a direct effect on blood cholesterol levels, in fact the best way to reduce blood cholesterol is to eat less saturated fat and to increase intake of foods containing soluble fibre.

Fat Although a small amount of fat is essential for good health, most people consume far too much. Healthy eating guidelines recommend that no more than 33% of our daily energy intake (calories) should come from fat. Each gram of fat contains 9 kcal, more than twice as many calories as carbohydrate or protein, so for a woman aged 19–49 years this means a daily maximum of 71 g fat, and for a man in the same age range 93.5 g fat.

Fats can be divided into 3 main groups: saturated, monounsaturated and polyunsaturated, depending on the chemical structure of the fatty acids they contain. *Saturated fatty acids* are found mainly in animal fats such as butter and other dairy products and in fatty meat. A high intake of saturated fat is known to be a risk factor for coronary heart disease and certain types of cancer. Current guidelines are that no more than 10% of our daily calories should come from saturated fats, which is about 21.5 g for an adult woman and 28.5 g for a man.

Where saturated fats tend to be solid at room temperature, the *unsaturated fatty acids* – monounsaturated and polyunsaturated – tend to be liquid. *Monounsaturated fats* are found predominantly in olive oil, groundnut (peanut) oil, rapeseed oil and avocados. Foods high in *polyunsaturates* include most vegetable oils – the exceptions are palm oil and coconut oil, both of which are saturated.

Both saturated and monounsaturated fatty acids can be made by the body, but certain polyunsaturated fatty acids – known as *essential fatty acids* – must be supplied by food. There are 2 'families' of these essential fatty acids: *omega-6*, derived from linoleic acid, and *omega-3*, from linolenic acid. The main food sources of the omega-6 family are vegetable oils such as olive and sunflower; omega-3 fatty acids are provided by oily fish, nuts, and vegetable oils such as soya and rapeseed.

When vegetable oils are hydrogenated (hardened) to make margarine and reduced-fat spreads, their unsaturated fatty acids can be changed into trans fatty acids, or '*trans fats*'. These artificially produced trans fats are believed to act in the same way as saturated fats within the body – with the same risks to health. Current healthy eating guidelines suggest that no more than 2% of our daily calories should come from trans fats, which is about 4.3 g for an adult woman and 5.6 g for a man. In thinking about the amount of trans fats you consume, remember that major sources are processed foods such as biscuits, pies, cakes and crisps.

Fibre Technically non-starch polysaccharides (NSP), fibre is the term commonly used to describe several different compounds, such as pectin, hemicellulose, lignin and gums, which are found in the cell walls of all plants. The body cannot digest fibre, nor does it have much nutritional value, but it plays an important role in helping us to stay healthy.

Fibre can be divided into 2 groups – soluble and insoluble. Both types are provided by most plant foods, but some foods are particularly good sources of one type or the other. *Soluble fibre* (in oats, pulses, fruit and vegetables) can help to reduce high blood cholesterol levels and to control blood sugar levels by slowing down the absorption of sugar. *Insoluble fibre* (in wholegrain cereals, pulses, fruit and vegetables) increases stool bulk and speeds the passage of waste material through the body. In this way it helps to prevent constipation, haemorrhoids and diverticular disease, and may protect against bowel cancer.

Our current intake of fibre is around 12 g a day. Healthy eating guidelines suggest that we need to increase this amount to 18 g a day.

Free radicals These highly reactive molecules can cause damage to cell walls and DNA (the genetic material found within cells). They are believed to be involved in the development of heart disease, some cancers and premature ageing. Free radicals are produced naturally by the body in the course of everyday life, but certain factors, such as cigarette smoke, pollution and over-exposure to sunlight, can accelerate their production.

Gluten A protein found in wheat and, to a lesser degree, in rye, barley and oats, but not in corn (maize) or rice. People with *coeliac disease* have a sensitivity to gluten and need to eliminate all gluten-containing foods, such as bread, pasta, cakes and biscuits, from their diet.

Glycaemic Index (GI) This is used to measure the rate at which carbohydrate foods are digested and converted into sugar (glucose) to raise blood sugar levels and provide energy. Foods with a high GI are quickly broken down and offer an immediate energy fix, while those with a lower GI are absorbed more slowly, making you feel full for longer and helping to keep blood sugar levels constant. High-GI foods include table sugar, honey, mashed potatoes and watermelon. Low-GI foods include pulses, wholewheat cereals, apples, cherries, dried apricots, pasta and oats.

Glycogen This is one of the 2 forms in which energy from carbohydrates is made available for use by the body (the other is *glucose*). Whereas glucose is converted quickly from carbohydrates and made available in the blood for a fast energy fix, glycogen is stored in the liver and muscles to fuel longer-term energy needs. When the body has used up its immediate supply of glucose, the stored glycogen is broken down into glucose to continue supplying energy.

Minerals These inorganic substances perform a wide range of vital functions in the body. The *macrominerals* – calcium, chloride, magnesium, potassium, phosphorus and sodium – are needed in relatively large quantities, whereas much smaller amounts are required of the remainder, called *microminerals*. Some microminerals (selenium, magnesium and iodine, for example) are needed in such tiny amounts that they are known as *'trace elements'*.

There are important differences in the body's ability to absorb minerals from different foods, and this can be affected by the presence of other substances. For example, oxalic acid, present in spinach, interferes with the absorption of much of the iron and calcium spinach contains.
• *Calcium* is essential for the development of strong bones and teeth. It also plays an important role in blood clotting. Good sources include dairy products, canned fish (eaten with their bones) and dark green, leafy vegetables.
• *Chloride* helps to maintain the body's fluid balance. The main source in the diet is table salt.
• *Chromium* is important in the regulation of blood sugar levels, as well as levels of fat and cholesterol in the blood. Good dietary sources include red meat, liver, eggs, seafood, cheese and wholegrain cereals.

• *Copper*, component of many enzymes, is needed for bone growth and the formation of connective tissue. It helps the body to absorb iron from food. Good sources include offal, shellfish, mushrooms, cocoa, nuts and seeds.
• *Iodine* is an important component of the thyroid hormones, which govern the rate and efficiency at which food is converted into energy. Good sources include seafood, seaweed and vegetables (depending on the iodine content of the soil in which they are grown).
• *Iron* is an essential component of haemoglobin, the pigment in red blood cells that carries oxygen around the body. Good sources are offal, red meat, dried apricots and prunes, and iron-fortified breakfast cereals.
• *Magnesium* is important for healthy bones, the release of energy from food, and nerve and muscle function. Good sources include wholegrain cereals, peas and other green vegetables, pulses, dried fruit and nuts.
• *Manganese* is a vital component of several enzymes that are involved in energy production and many other functions. Good dietary sources include nuts, cereals, brown rice, pulses and wholemeal bread.
• *Molybdenum* is an essential component of several enzymes, including those involved in the production of DNA. Good sources are offal, yeast, pulses, wholegrain cereals and green leafy vegetables.
• *Phosphorus* is important for healthy bones and teeth and for the release of energy from foods. It is found in most foods. Particularly good sources include dairy products, red meat, poultry, fish and eggs.
• *Potassium*, along with sodium, is important in maintaining fluid balance and regulating blood pressure, and is essential for the transmission of nerve impulses. Good sources include fruit, especially bananas and citrus fruits, nuts, seeds, potatoes and pulses.
• *Selenium* is a powerful antioxidant that protects cells against damage by free radicals. Good dietary sources are meat, fish, dairy foods, brazil nuts, avocados and lentils.
• *Sodium* works with potassium to regulate fluid balance, and is essential for nerve and muscle function. Only a little sodium is needed – we tend to get too much in our diet. The main source in the diet is table salt, as well as salty processed foods and ready-prepared foods.
• *Sulphur* is a component of 2 essential amino acids. Protein foods are the main source.
• *Zinc* is vital for normal growth, as well as reproduction and immunity. Good dietary sources include oysters, red meat, peanuts and sunflower seeds.

Phytochemicals These biologically active compounds, found in most plant foods, are believed to be beneficial in disease prevention. There are literally thousands of different phytochemicals, amongst which are the following:

• *Allicin*, a phytochemical found in garlic, onions, leeks, chives and shallots, is believed to help lower high blood cholesterol levels and stimulate the immune system.
• *Bioflavonoids*, of which there are at least 6000, are found mainly in fruit and sweet-tasting vegetables. Different bioflavonoids have different roles – some are antioxidants, while others act as anti-disease agents. A sub-group of these phytochemicals, called *flavonols*, includes the antioxidant *quercetin*, which is believed to reduce the risk of heart disease and help to protect against cataracts. Quercetin is found in tea, red wine, grapes and broad beans.
• *Carotenoids*, the best known of which are *beta-carotene* and *lycopene*, are powerful antioxidants thought to help protect us against certain types of cancer. Highly coloured fruits and vegetables, such as blackcurrants, mangoes, tomatoes, carrots, sweet potatoes, pumpkin and dark green, leafy vegetables, are excellent sources of carotenoids.
• *Coumarins* are believed to help protect against cancer by inhibiting the formation of tumours. Oranges are a rich source.
• *Glucosinolates*, found mainly in cruciferous vegetables, particularly broccoli, Brussels sprouts, cabbage, kale and cauliflower, are believed to have strong anti-cancer effects. *Sulphoraphane* is one of the powerful cancer-fighting substances produced by glucosinolates.
• *Phytoestrogens* have a chemical structure similar to the female hormone oestrogen, and they are believed to help protect against hormone-related cancers such as breast and prostate cancer. One of the types of these phytochemicals, called *isoflavones*, may also help to relieve symptoms associated with the menopause. Soya beans and chickpeas are a particularly rich source of isoflavones.

Protein This nutrient, necessary for growth and development, for maintenance and repair of cells, and for the production of enzymes, antibodies and hormones, is essential to keep the body working efficiently. Protein is made up of *amino acids*, which are compounds containing the 4 elements that are necessary for life: carbon, hydrogen, oxygen and nitrogen. We need all of the 20 amino acids commonly found in plant and animal proteins. The human body can make 12 of these, but the remaining 8 – called *essential amino acids* – must be obtained from the food we eat.

Protein comes in a wide variety of foods. Meat, fish, dairy products, eggs and soya beans contain all of the essential amino acids, and are therefore called first-class protein foods. Pulses, nuts, seeds and cereals are also good sources of protein, but do not contain the full range of essential amino acids. In practical terms, this really doesn't matter – as long as you include a variety of different protein foods in your diet, your body will get all the amino acids it needs. It is important, though, to eat protein foods every day because the essential amino acids cannot be stored in the body for later use.

The RNI of protein for women aged 19–49 years is 45 g per day and for men of the same age 55 g. In the UK most people eat more protein than they need, although this isn't normally a problem.

Reference Nutrient Intake (RNI) This denotes the average daily amount of vitamins and minerals thought to be sufficient to meet the nutritional needs of almost all individuals within the population. The figures, published by the Department of Health, vary depending on age, sex and specific nutritional needs such as pregnancy. RNIs are equivalent to what used to be called Recommended Daily Amounts or Allowances (RDA).

RNIs for adults (19–49 years)

Vitamin A	600–700 mcg
Vitamin B_1	0.8 mg for women, 1 mg for men
Vitamin B_2	1.1 mg for women, 1.3 mg for men
Niacin	13 mg for women, 17 mg for men
Vitamin B_6	1.2 mg for women, 1.4 mg for men
Vitamin B_{12}	1.5 mg
Folate	200 mcg (400 mcg for first trimester of pregnancy)
Vitamin C	40 mg
Vitamin E	no recommendation in the UK; the EC RDA is 10 mg, which has been used in all recipe analyses in this book
Calcium	700 mg
Chloride	2500 mg
Copper	1.2 mg
Iodine	140 mcg
Iron	14.8 mg for women, 8.7 mg for men
Magnesium	270–300 mg
Phosphorus	550 mg
Potassium	3500 mg
Selenium	60 mcg for women, 75 mcg for men
Sodium	1600 mg
Zinc	7 mg for women, 9.5 mg for men

Vitamins These are organic compounds that are essential for good health. Although they are required in only small amounts, each one has specific vital functions to perform. Most vitamins cannot be made by the human body, and therefore must be obtained from the diet. The body is capable of storing some vitamins (A, D, E, K and B_{12}), but the rest need to be provided by the diet on a regular basis. A well-balanced diet, containing a wide variety of different foods, is the best way to ensure that you get all the vitamins you need.

Vitamins can be divided into 2 groups: *water-soluble* (B complex and C) and *fat-soluble* (A, D, E and K). Water-soluble vitamins are easily destroyed during processing, storage, and the preparation and cooking of food. The fat-soluble vitamins are less vulnerable to losses during cooking and processing.

• *Vitamin A* (retinol) is essential for healthy vision, eyes, skin and growth. Good sources include dairy products, offal (especially liver), eggs and oily fish. Vitamin A can also be obtained from *beta-carotene*, the pigment found in highly coloured fruit and vegetables. In addition to acting as a source of vitamin A, beta-carotene has an important role to play as an antioxidant in its own right.

• *The B Complex vitamins* have very similar roles to play in nutrition, and many of them occur together in the same foods.
Vitamin B_1 (thiamin) is essential in the release of energy from carbohydrates. Good sources include milk, offal, meat (especially pork), wholegrain and fortified breakfast cereals, nuts and pulses, yeast extract and wheat germ. White flour and bread are fortified with B_1 in the UK.
Vitamin B_2 (riboflavin) is vital for growth, healthy skin and eyes, and the release of energy from food. Good sources include milk, meat, offal, eggs, cheese, fortified breakfast cereals, yeast extract and green leafy vegetables.
Niacin (nicotinic acid), sometimes called vitamin B_3, plays an important role in the release of energy within the cells. Unlike the other B vitamins it can be made by the body from the essential amino acid tryptophan. Good sources include meat, offal, fish, fortified breakfast cereals and pulses. White flour and bread are fortified with niacin in the UK.
Pantothenic acid, sometimes called vitamin B_5, is involved in a number of metabolic reactions, including energy production. This vitamin is present in most foods; notable exceptions are fat, oil and sugar. Good sources include liver, kidneys, yeast, egg yolks, fish roe, wheat germ, nuts, pulses and fresh vegetables.
Vitamin B_6 (pyridoxine) helps the body to utilise protein and contributes to the formation of haemoglobin for red blood cells. B_6 is found in a wide range of foods including meat, liver, fish, eggs, wholegrain cereals, some vegetables, pulses, brown rice, nuts and yeast extract.
Vitamin B_{12} (cyanocobalamin) is vital for growth, the formation of red blood cells and maintenance of a healthy nervous system. B_{12} is unique in that it is only found in foods of animal origin. Vegetarians who eat dairy products will get enough, but vegans need to ensure they include food fortified with B_{12} in their diet. Good sources of B_{12} include liver, kidneys, oily fish, meat, cheese, eggs and milk.
Folate (folic acid) is involved in the manufacture of amino acids and in the production of red blood cells. Recent research suggests that folate may also help to protect against heart disease. Good sources of folate are

green leafy vegetables, liver, pulses, eggs, wholegrain cereal products and fortified breakfast cereals, brewers' yeast, wheatgerm, nuts and fruit, especially grapefruit and oranges.
Biotin is needed for various metabolic reactions and the release of energy from foods. Good sources include liver, oily fish, brewers' yeast, kidneys, egg yolks and brown rice.

• *Vitamin C* (ascorbic acid) is essential for growth and vital for the formation of collagen (a protein needed for healthy bones, teeth, gums, blood capillaries and all connective tissue). It plays an important role in the healing of wounds and fractures, and acts as a powerful antioxidant. Vitamin C is found mainly in fruit and vegetables.

• *Vitamin D* (cholecalciferol) is essential for growth and the absorption of calcium, and thus for the formation of healthy bones. It is also involved in maintaining a healthy nervous system. The amount of vitamin D occurring naturally in foods is small, and it is found in very few foods – good sources are oily fish (and fish liver oil supplements), eggs and liver, as well as breakfast cereals, margarine and full-fat milk that are fortified with vitamin D. Most vitamin D, however, does not come from the diet but is made by the body when the skin is exposed to sunlight.

• *Vitamin E* is not one vitamin, but a number of related compounds called tocopherols that function as antioxidants. Good sources of vitamin E are vegetable oils, polyunsaturated margarines, wheatgerm, sunflower seeds, nuts, oily fish, eggs, wholegrain cereals, avocados and spinach.

• *Vitamin K* is essential for the production of several proteins, including prothombin which is involved in the clotting of blood. It has been found to exist in 3 forms, one of which is obtained from food while the other 2 are made by the bacteria in the intestine. Vitamin K_1, which is the form found in food, is present in broccoli, cabbage, spinach, milk, margarine, vegetable oils, particularly soya oil, cereals, liver, alfalfa and kelp.

Nutritional analyses

The nutritional analysis of each recipe has been carried out using data from *The Composition of Foods* with additional data from food manufacturers where appropriate. Because the level and availability of different nutrients can vary, depending on factors like growing conditions and breed of animal, the figures are intended as an approximate guide only.

The analyses include vitamins A, B_1, B_2, B_6, B_{12}, niacin, folate, C, D and E, and the minerals calcium, copper, iron, potassium, selenium and zinc. Other vitamins and minerals are not included, as deficiencies are rare. Optional ingredients and optional serving suggestions have not been included in the calculations.

Index

*Printing and binding: Printer Industria Grafica
    S.A., Barcelona
Separations: Litho Origination, London
Paper: Perigord-Condat, France*

index